Gill SKILLS

# SUPER SLEUTH

6TH CLASS



Audrey Cooney

GILL EDUCATION

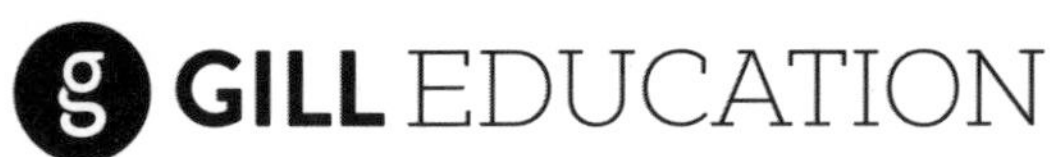

**Gill Education**
**Hume Avenue**
**Park West**
**Dublin 12**
**www.gilleducation.ie**

Gill Education is an imprint of M.H. Gill & Co.



**ISBN:** 978-0-7171-71804



**Editor:** Donna Garvin

**Design and layout:** Liz White Designs

**Illustrations:** Derry Dillon

**Cover design:** Slickfish

**Cover illustration:** Derry Dillon

For permission to reproduce photographs, the author and publisher gratefully acknowledge the following:

© Alamy: 15, 28, 67R; © Getty Images: 67L; © iStock: 31, 97.

The author and publisher have made every effort to trace all copyright holders. If, however, any have been inadvertently overlooked, we would be pleased to make the necessary arrangement at the first opportunity.

The paper used in this book is made from the wood pulp of managed forests. For every tree felled, at least one tree is planted, thereby renewing natural resources.

# Contents

# How to Use this Book

*Super Sleuth* is a unique mathematical problem-solving series for 1st to 6th Class primary school pupils. Problem-solving requires pupils to understand and explore a problem, find a strategy, use the strategy to solve the problem and look back and reflect on the solution. *Super Sleuth* focuses on the process of problem-solving and the development of the **ten main problem-solving strategies**. The series has **regular built-in revision** units, which consolidate problem-solving skills.

## Differentiation   

Differentiation is catered for in each unit through the use of **bronze**, **silver** and **gold** medals that indicate the level of difficulty and provide an entry point for every pupil as well as opportunities for **high-achievers** to be challenged.

## Collaborative learning

**The series facilitates collaborative learning** through **whole-class**, **pair** and **group work** activities. This creates an ideal classroom environment for pupils to develop their maths language and thinking, in which the teacher can act as facilitator and every pupil's contribution is valued. Learning can be applied at home through practice.

## Dedicated strategy units 

Each book dedicates **five units to a specific strategy** and pupils are encouraged to utilise and apply the strategies where relevant.

## Super Sleuth's ten problem-solving strategies:

- Trial and improvement
- Working backwards
- Working systematically
- Logical reasoning
- Visualising/Draw a picture

- Patterns
- Make a table
- Act it out
- Make a model
- Simplify

## CLUES

CLUES is a teacher- and pupil-friendly **framework** developed uniquely for *Super Sleuth* to tackle the most common **problem-solving difficulties** experienced in the classroom. It was created in order to promote Bloom's higher forms of thinking in maths education.

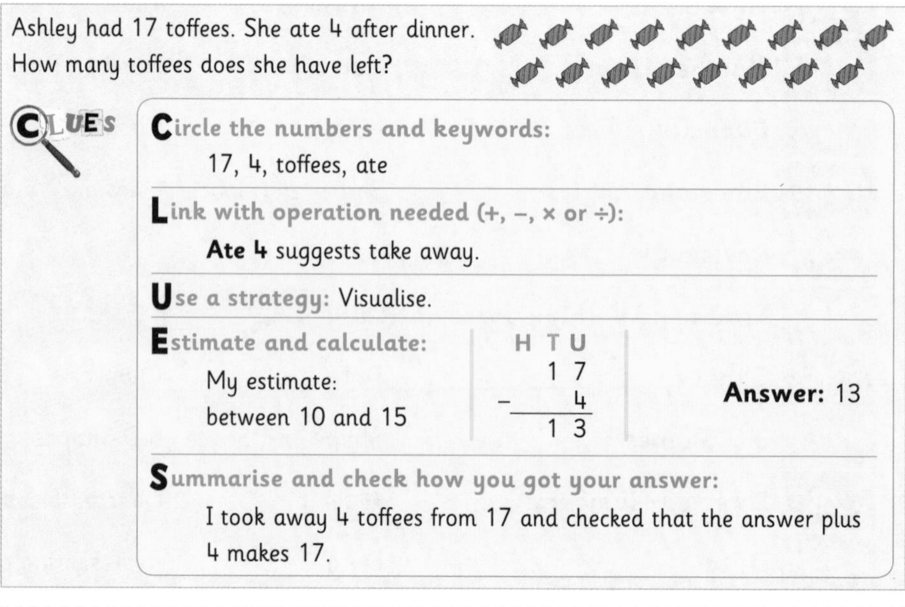

## Super Sleuth key features

**Weekly structure:** Weekly arrangement of work (30 units) and provides four days of work with three to four questions per day.

**WALT:** Clear learning outcomes are provided at the beginning of each new strand.

**Worked example:** A worked example using the CLUES framework is provided at the start of new strands to demonstrate a strategy that pupils can follow, allowing them to work independently.

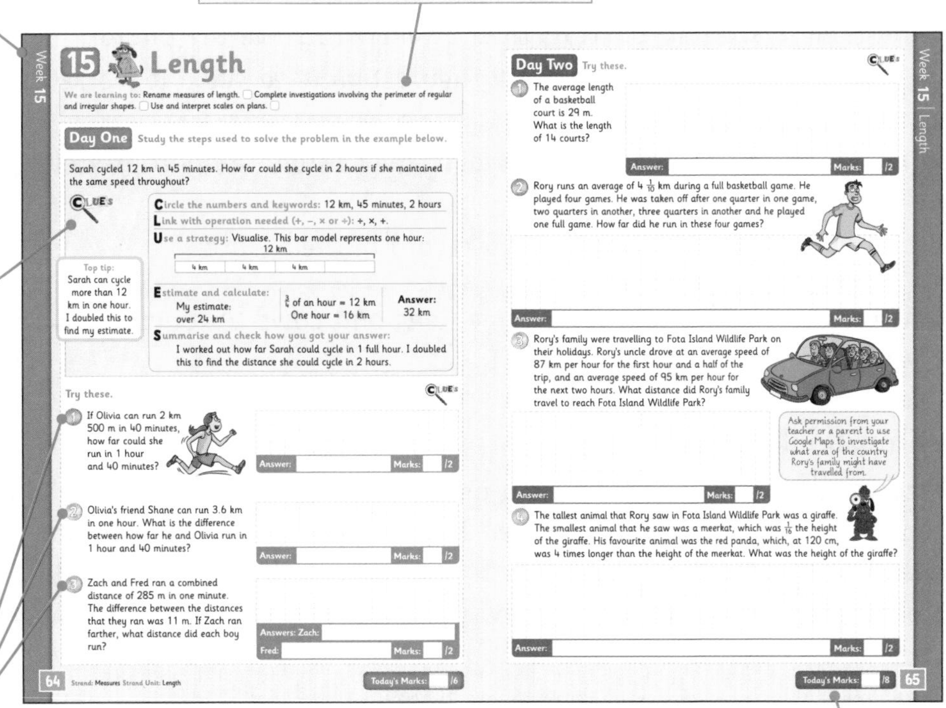
Week 15

15 Length

We are learning to: Rename measures of length. Complete investigations involving the perimeter of regular and irregular shapes. Use and interpret scales on plans.

Day One Study the steps used to solve the problem in the example below.

Sarah cycled 12 km in 45 minutes. How far could she cycle in 2 hours if she maintained the same speed throughout?

Circle the numbers and keywords: 12 km, 45 minutes, 2 hours

Link with operation needed (+, –, × or ÷): +, ×, +.

Use a strategy: Visualise. This bar model represents one hour: 12 km

4 km 4 km 4 km

Top tip: Sarah can cycle more than 12 km in one hour. I doubled this to find my estimate.

Estimate and calculate: My estimate: over 24 km $\frac{3}{4}$ of an hour = 12 km One hour = 16 km Answer: 32 km

Summarise and check how you got your answer: I worked out how far Sarah could cycle in 1 full hour. I doubled this to find the distance she could cycle in 2 hours.

Try these.

1. If Olivia can run 2 km 500 m in 40 minutes, how far could she run in 1 hour and 40 minutes? Answer: Marks: /2

2. Olivia's friend Shane can run 3.6 km in one hour. What is the difference between how far he and Olivia run in 1 hour and 40 minutes? Answer: Marks: /2

3. Zach and Fred ran a combined distance of 285 m in one minute. The difference between the distances that they ran was 11 m. If Zach ran farther, what distance did each boy run? Answers: Zach: Fred: Marks: /2

64 Strand: Measures Strand Unit: Length Today's Marks: /6

Day Two Try these.

1. The average length of a basketball court is 29 m. What is the length of 14 courts? Answer: Marks: /2

2. Rory runs an average of 4 $\frac{1}{10}$ km during a full basketball game. He played four games. He was taken off after one quarter in one game, two quarters in another, three quarters in another and he played one full game. How far did he run in these four games? Answer: Marks: /2

3. Rory's family were travelling to Fota Island Wildlife Park on their holidays. Rory's uncle drove at an average speed of 87 km per hour for the first hour and a half of the trip, and an average speed of 95 km per hour for the next two hours. What distance did Rory's family travel to reach Fota Island Wildlife Park? Answer: Marks: /2

Ask permission from your teacher or a parent to use Google Maps to investigate what area of the country Rory's family might have travelled from.

4. The tallest animal that Rory saw in Fota Island Wildlife Park was a giraffe. The smallest animal that he saw was a meerkat, which was $\frac{1}{16}$ the height of the giraffe. His favourite animal was the red panda, which, at 120 cm, was 4 times longer than the height of the meerkat. What was the height of the giraffe? Answer: Marks: /2

Today's Marks: /8 65

Week 15 | Length

**Clear differentiation:** Each page is differentiated using bronze, silver and gold medals to show the level of difficulty and give pupils an incentive to progress. The bronze medal indicates a question that the majority of the class should work on independently. The silver medal poses more of a challenge, while the gold medal may require collaborative work in order for the pupils to reach a solution.

**Progress recording:** Each question and week has a score tracker to help pupils self-assess.

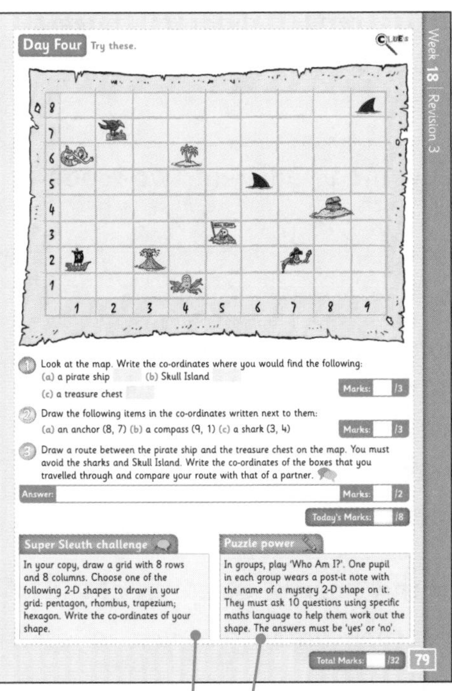
Day Four Try these.

1. Look at the map. Write the co-ordinates where you would find the following: (a) a pirate ship (b) Skull Island (c) a treasure chest Marks: /3

2. Draw the following items in the co-ordinates written next to them: (a) an anchor (8, 7) (b) a compass (9, 1) (c) a shark (3, 4) Marks: /3

3. Draw a route between the pirate ship and the treasure chest on the map. You must avoid the sharks and Skull Island. Write the co-ordinates of the boxes that you travelled through and compare your route with that of a partner. Answer: Marks: /2

Today's Marks: /8

Super Sleuth challenge: In your copy, draw a grid with 8 rows and 8 columns. Choose one of the following 2-D shapes to draw in your grid: pentagon, rhombus, trapezium, hexagon. Write the co-ordinates of your shape.

Puzzle power: In groups, play 'Who Am I?'. One pupil in each group wears a post-it note with the name of a mystery 2-D shape on it. They must ask 10 questions using specific maths language to help them work out the shape. The answers must be 'yes' or 'no'.

Total Marks: /32 79

Week 18 | Revision 3

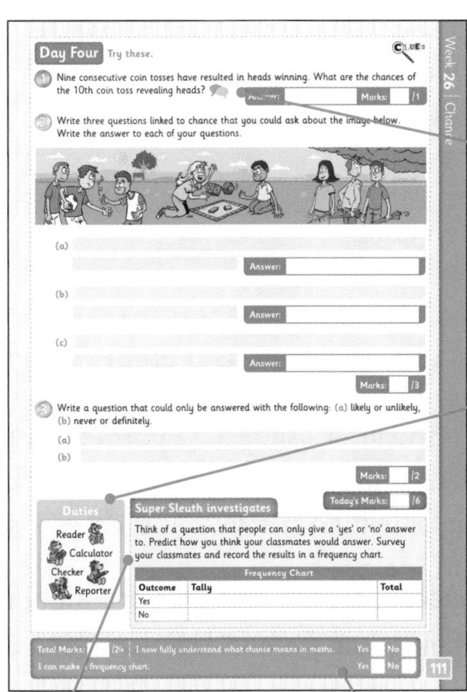
Day Four Try these.

1. Nine consecutive coin tosses have resulted in heads winning. What are the chances of the 10th coin toss revealing heads? Answer: Marks: /1

2. Write three questions linked to chance that you could ask about the image below. Write the answer to each of your questions. (a) Answer: (b) Answer: (c) Answer: Marks: /3

3. Write a question that could only be answered with the following: (a) likely or unlikely, (b) never or definitely. (a) (b) Marks: /2

Today's Marks: /6

Duties: Reader, Calculator, Checker, Reporter

Super Sleuth investigates: Think of a question that people can only give a 'yes' or 'no' answer to. Predict how you think your classmates would answer. Survey your classmates and record the results in a frequency chart.

Frequency Chart

| Outcome | Tally | Total |
|---|---|---|
| Yes | | |
| No | | |

Total Marks: /24 I now fully understand what chance means in maths. Yes No

I can make a frequency chart. Yes No

111

Week 26 | Chance

**Pair work/group work:** Opportunities are provided for pair and group work. Group work can be applied to activities and these specific questions are highlighted throughout the book, where different roles can be assigned to up to four pupils.

**Puzzles and challenges:** 'Super Sleuth challenge' is an open-ended question based on the maths skills and strand covered in the unit. 'Super Sleuth investigates' is an activity for applying the maths skills/strand of the unit to a situation that could be encountered in real life.

**Self-assessment:** The self-assessment section for each strand offers pupils an opportunity to reflect on their learning, as well as providing very valuable information to the teacher.

# Problem-solving strategies

## Trial and improvement

- The strategy of trial and improvement encourages pupils to make a reasonable estimate, giving them a starting point as they attempt to solve the puzzle.
- The pupils are then asked to check their estimate to see if it works as a solution and revise it accordingly.
- By repeating this process and changing their estimate appropriately, pupils should arrive at the correct answer.
- All rough work should be kept as a record of their work.

**Example:** On a farm there were some hens and cows. Altogether there were 8 heads and 22 feet. How many hens were there?

## Working backwards

- Occasionally pupils come across a puzzle in which they are given the final answer and the steps taken to arrive at the answer, but they are not given the data from the start of the puzzle. They must undo each step to get back to the starting point.
- Pupils can draw a diagram to show the known facts and use the inverse operation when working backwards.

**Example:** Martha removed a loaf of bread from the oven after it had been baking for two hours. If she took it out at 4 o'clock, at what time did she put it into the oven?

## Working systematically

- Working systematically requires pupils to work carefully through the information they are given.
- This strategy may incorporate other strategies for pupils to draw upon in order to work out the process of the problem. They might need to make a list, draw a diagram, make a table or explore problems with numerous answers in order to organise and build on the information until they find the solution.

**Example:** There are six ice-cream flavours to choose from. How many different two-scoop ice-cream cones can be made?

## Logical reasoning

- Logical reasoning can be explained as a proper or reasonable way of thinking about something. It requires the pupils to think carefully about the information they have been given and decide on a way of using the information to solve the puzzle.
- Pupils are encouraged to use a step-by-step approach to reach a solution.
- This may involve implementing a strategy such as visualisation or making a table.

**Example:** Grumpy, Sneezy, Sleepy and Doc are all in line for the cinema. Sleepy is ahead of Grumpy, Sneezy is behind Grumpy and Doc is second. What is their order from first to last?

## Visualising / Draw a picture

- Drawing a diagram can help pupils to visualise a puzzle. By doing this, they can make connections within the puzzle and plan how to solve it.
- Diagrams can include tree diagrams, timelines, pictures, symbols and Venn diagrams.

**Example:** Felix made 12 butterfly buns and iced them. He placed two chocolate buttons on top of each bun. How many chocolate buttons did he use?

### Patterns

- This strategy involves pupils investigating how numbers, images or symbols are arranged in a variety of orders.
- Each pattern follows a rule. Pupils may be asked to identify the rule in a pattern, find the missing value(s) or extend the existing pattern. Many things in our world follow a set of rules, so that we know what to expect.

**Example:** Millie is making a beaded necklace that follows a pattern of red, green, blue. If she uses 18 beads in total, how many red beads will she use?

### Make a table

- When puzzles are written in word sentences, they can be confusing for pupils.
- Making a table helps pupils to organise the information that they have and identify the information that they need.

**Example:** Mikey saves €4 on Monday. Each day after that, he saves twice as much as the day before. How much money will he have saved by Friday?

### Act it out

- Acting it out is an effective strategy for pupils who have difficulty visualising a problem.
- Acting out a problem using props such as cubes or string, or in pairs or groups can greatly simplify finding solutions and is an effective strategy for demonstration purposes in front of the whole class.

**Example:** I have a 5 litre jug and a 3 litre jug. How can I measure out 7 litres of juice using these jugs?

### Make a model

- By making a model, the pupils are given an opportunity to showcase their understanding of a specific area of maths. For example, pupils can investigate the properties of 3-D shapes through model building.

**Example:** Using 26 cocktail sticks and Blu-tack, how many cubes can Emily make and how many cocktail sticks will be left over?

### Simplify

There are three ways in which pupils can simplify a puzzle:

- Reword the puzzle using a more familiar setting.
- Break the puzzle down into steps and solve one part at a time.
- Use smaller numbers.

**Example:** Amy spent $\frac{1}{8}$ of her savings on a new jacket. If she had €320 in savings, how much did the jacket cost?

$\frac{1}{8}$ of €32 = €4 → $\frac{1}{8}$ of €320 = €40

# 1 Strategy: Logical Reasoning

## Day One

When using logical reasoning to solve puzzles, you use a step-by-step approach to reach the solution. This may involve drawing a matrix (a type of grid), making a list or using a diagram to help. You might also make a prediction and test if this was correct.

**Try these.**

CLUES

1. Look at this image of a computer game. The names of these characters are Rod, Lala, Jolly and Tide. Use the following clue to work out which one is which: Tide is located south of Rod and east of Lala.

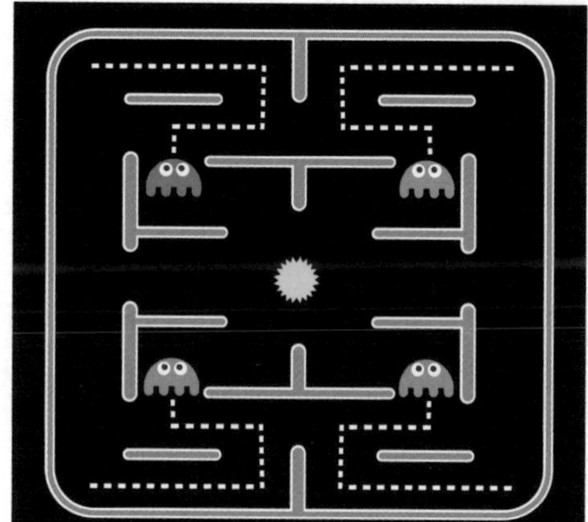

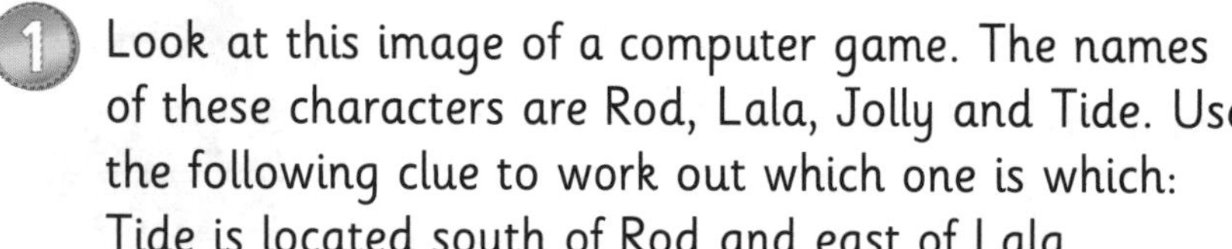

**Answers: Red** ______ **Blue** ______
**Orange** ______ **Green** ______ **Marks:** ___ /4

2. Figure out what score each of these four characters got.
   - Jolly and Tide's combined score was 11,450.
   - Jolly, Tide and Rod's combined score was 15,934.
   - Jolly's score was 100 points less than Tide's score.
   - The total number of points scored was 20,554.

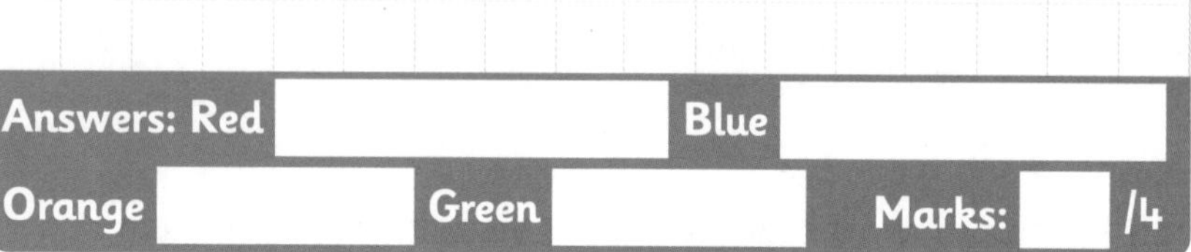

**Answers: Jolly** ______ **Tide** ______ **Rod** ______ **Lala** ______ **Marks:** ___ /4

3. Using the information above, place the names of the characters into the Venn diagram in the suitable sections based on their score.

> **Top tip:** A palindromic number reads the same in both directions, e.g. 4,224.

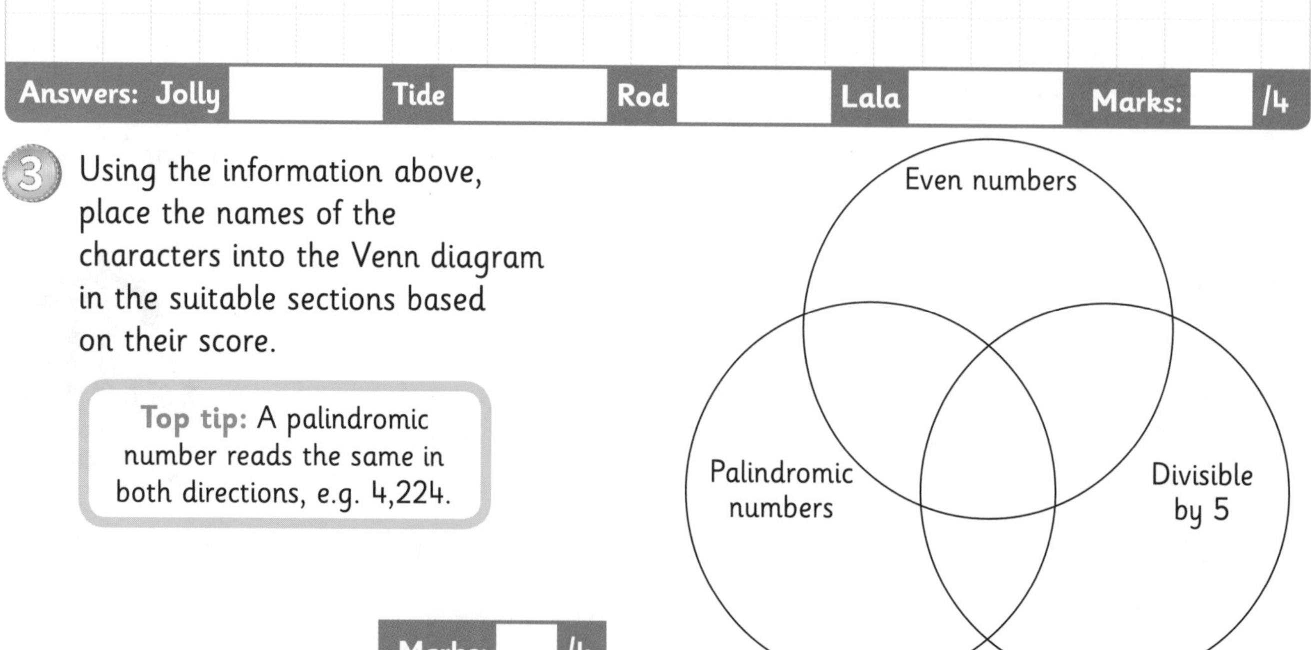


**Marks:** ___ /4



**Today's Marks:** ___ /12

## Day Two Try these.

You could use matchsticks or straws to help you solve these visual puzzles.

CLUES

Here is an example of a popular matchstick puzzle. Look at how it is solved.

Move just two matchsticks to recreate the same shape with the matchsticks, but leave the coin outside of the shape.

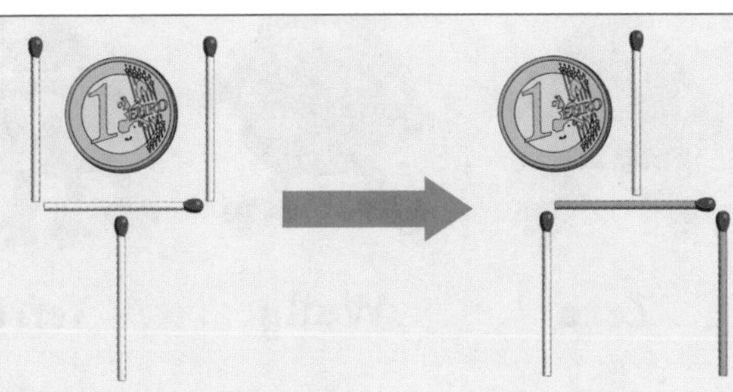

1. Move just two matchsticks to create 7 squares. (Matchsticks may overlap.)

Marks: /2

2. Move just three matchsticks to create 3 squares of equal size. (Matchsticks may **not** overlap.)

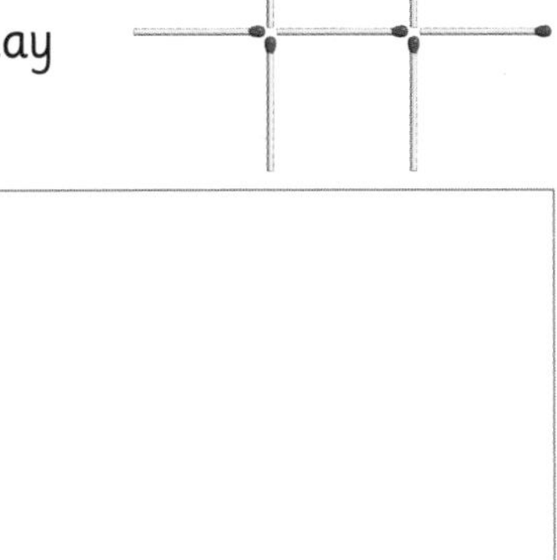

Marks: /2

3. Move just three matchsticks to create 4 triangles. (Matchsticks may **not** overlap.)

Marks: /2

4. Move just three matchsticks to create 4 squares of equal size. (Matchsticks may **not** overlap. None will be left over if you do this correctly.)

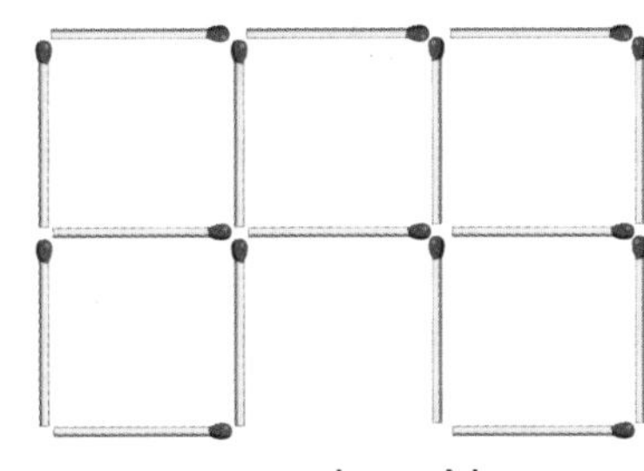

Marks: /2

### Super Sleuth challenge

Create the tallest paper tower that you can, using 10 A4 sheets of paper and paper clips. Your paper tower cannot lean against an object for support and must be able to stand by itself for 10 seconds while being measured.

Today's Marks: /8

## Day Three Try these.

**1** Write the names of the aliens in the suitable sections of the Venn diagram.

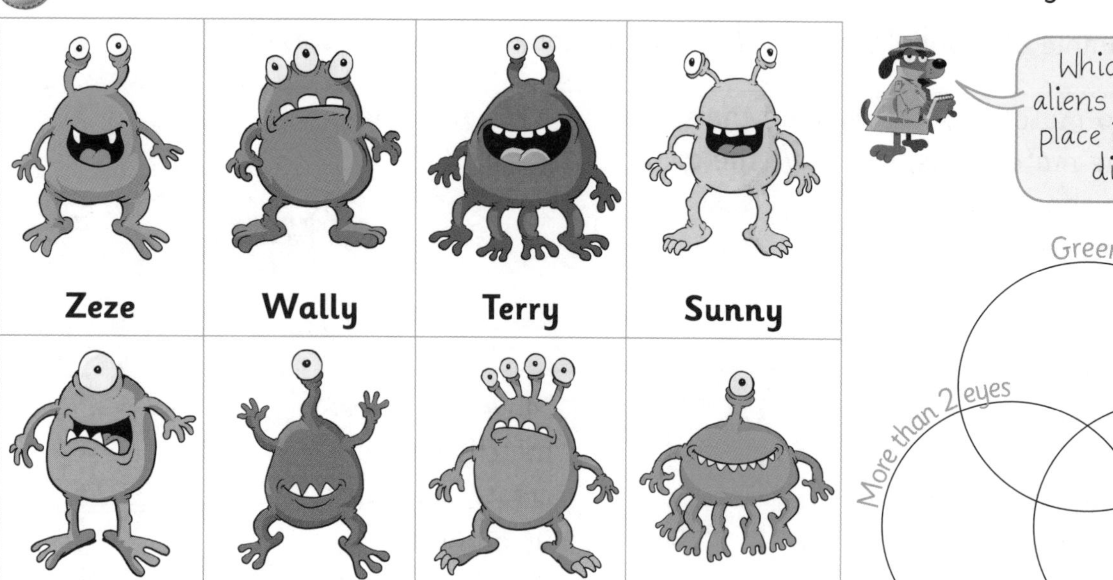


Which of these aliens can you not place in the Venn diagram?

Green

More than 2 eyes

2 legs

Marks: /8

**2** Use the matrix to work out four of the aliens' jobs. Once you can rule out information, place an 'X' in the box in the matrix. When you are confident that you know an alien's job, tick (✓) the box in the matrix.

| | Doctor | Pilot | Scientist | Hairdresser |
|---|---|---|---|---|
| **Zeze** | | | | |
| **Terry** | | | | |
| **Sunny** | | | | |
| **Spot** | | | | |

- Terry is afraid of flying.
- Sunny works in a laboratory.
- Spot is not a doctor and neither is Zeze.
- Zeze travels all over the galaxy.

Marks: /4

**3** Wally, Rosie, Spot, Smiley and Cyclops each live within 20 km directly east or west of Roswell Shopping Centre. Can you work out how far each of these aliens travels to the shopping centre using the clues below?

- Rosie lives 20 km west of Wally and Cyclops lives 7 km east of Wally.
- Smiley lives 21 km west of Cyclops and 9 km west of Roswell Shopping Centre.
- Spot lives 33 km east of Rosie.

| Rosie | Spot | Smiley | Wally | Cyclops |
|---|---|---|---|---|
| | | | | |

Marks: /10



Today's Marks: /22

## Day Four Try these.

The aim of Sudoku is to insert numbers into a grid horizontally, vertically and in groups, ensuring that every number appears once in each row, column and group.

1. In this Sudoku puzzle, you will use the numbers 1–6.

| | | | | | |
|---|---|---|---|---|---|
| | | 3 | 1 | | |
| 3 | 1 | | | 4 | |
| 2 | | | 4 | | 1 |
| 4 | | | | | 6 |
| | 2 | | | 5 | 3 |
| | | 2 | | | |

Marks: /2

You can approach this puzzle by focusing on filling in the numbers in a row or a column. Other people like to focus on placing one number in the grid.

2. This Sudoku puzzle will require more work, as you will use the numbers 1–9.

| | | | | | | | | |
|---|---|---|---|---|---|---|---|---|
| 8 | | | 9 | 3 | | | | 2 |
| | | 9 | | | | | 4 | |
| 7 | | 2 | 1 | | | 9 | 6 | |
| 2 | | | | | | | 9 | |
| | 6 | | | | | | 7 | |
| | 7 | | | | 6 | | | 5 |
| | 2 | 7 | | | 8 | 4 | | 6 |
| | 3 | | | | | 5 | | |
| 5 | | | | 6 | 2 | | | 8 |

Marks: /2

Today's Marks: /4

### Duties

### Super Sleuth challenge

Eva cleaned an empty milk carton, decorated it and turned it into a money box. She just puts €1 coins into her money box. How many €1 coins do you think will fit in the milk carton? If she fills the milk carton with €1 coins, do you think she will have enough money to buy a bicycle for €250 or a laptop for €950? Discuss your opinion with your team and justify the reasons for your answer.

Total Marks: /46 | What are my strengths when I try to solve puzzles? For example, am I well organised? Can I think of different ways the puzzles could be solved? Do I know what strategy should be used?

How can my teacher assist me when solving puzzles?

# 2 Place Value

**We are learning to:** Read, write and order whole numbers and decimals. ☐
Identify place value in whole numbers and decimals. ☐ Round decimals to two or three decimal places. ☐

## Day One

**Try these.**

Use the strategy of logical reasoning to help solve the puzzles in this unit. Write your answers in word and expanded form in your copy.

CLUES

1. Using the digits in the image, what is the largest five-digit number that you can make?

5 5 8 8 7 5 2 9 9 3 4 1 3

**Answer:** ______ **Marks:** ___ /2

2. Using the digits in the image above, what is the largest six-digit number that you can make?

**Answer:** ______ **Marks:** ___ /2

3. What is the difference between your answers to questions 1 and 2 above?

**Top tip:** Be sure to place each digit in the correct family when subtracting.

**Answer:** ______ **Marks:** ___ /2

4. What number am I? Use the clues below to work out the answer.
   - I am an even six-digit number.
   - The digit in my ten-thousands family is $\frac{1}{3}$ the value of the digit in my hundreds family.
   - My hundreds digit minus my thousands digit gives you the value of the digit in my hundred-thousands family.
   - The digit in my units place is a square number.
   - The digit in my tens place is 4 less than the digit in my units place.
   - I have the digits 4, 2, 5, 0, 1 and 6 and am less than 200,000.

?

**Answer:** ______ **Marks:** ___ /2



**Today's Marks:** ___ /8

# Day Two Try these.

**1** Jan was shopping for a new guitar. The manager at Music to My Ears was offering a free guitar case to the first customer who could work out the price of a certain guitar using the clues below. **(a)** Can you help Jan to win the free guitar case by working out the price of the guitar?

- **Hundreds:** One-quarter the value of the units
- **Tens:** When you multiply this digit by itself, you get 36.
- **Units:** The number of sides on a pentagon plus the number of sides on a triangle
- **Tenths:** The square root of 81
- **Hundredths:** A number between 4 and 10 that has three factors

**(b)** What is the price of the guitar rounded to the nearest whole number?

**Answers: (a)** ____________ **(b)** ____________ **Marks:** ___ /4

**2** YouTube figures have been published showing the five most-viewed vloggers over the past month. Write the numbers in order, starting with the largest number of views.

| Xavier's Xbox Cheats | Mandy's Makeovers | Paul's Piano Perfection | Harry's Hair Hints | Immy's Impersonations |
|---|---|---|---|---|
| 119.175m | 119.017m | 118.952m | 119.201m | 119.122m |

**Answer:** ____________ **Marks:** ___ /1

**3** Write the value of the underlined digit in each of the following numbers:

**(a)** €1,4$\underline{5}$2,642 €____________

**(b)** 4.$\underline{8}$7 l ____________ ml

**(c)** $\underline{2}$09.85 km ____________ km

**Marks:** ___ /3

## Super Sleuth challenge

I added three numbers together that were each to three decimal places. The total was 6. What might the numbers have been?

**Today's Marks:** ___ /8

## Day Three

Try these.

Take my advice! Use the steps below to help you when rounding decimals.

CLUES

**Example:** Round 6.975 to two decimal places.

| 6.97 | 6.971 | 6.972 | 6.973 | 6.974 | **6.975** | 6.976 | 6.977 | 6.978 | 6.979 | 6.98 |
|---|---|---|---|---|---|---|---|---|---|---|

| | |
|---|---|
| **Underline the place.** | 6.9<u>7</u>5 |
| **Look at the neighbour to the right.** | We see the number 5. |
| **Remember the rounding rules.** | For 0 to 4, it stays the same forever more!<br>For 5 to 9, it moves one up the line! |
| **Make your decision.** | As the neighbour to the right is 5, this means we must change <u>7</u> to 8. |
| **Everything to the left stays the same.** | **Answer:** 6.98 |

Write each of your answers below to two decimal places.

1. If Dublin's Saint Patrick's Day parade route is 2.495 km long and New York City's parade route is 0.633 km longer, what is the length of New York City's route?

**Answer:** **Marks:** /2

2. Celine travelled 2,375 km to see the Saint Patrick's Day parade in Dublin. Her cousin Marie travelled $\frac{1}{8}$ of this distance. What distance did Marie travel?

**Answer:** **Marks:** /2

3. Sam's alarm didn't go off, so he was late joining his marching band for the parade! If they had already completed $\frac{2}{5}$ of the parade route in Dublin, what distance of the route did Sam complete?

**Answer:** **Marks:** /2

### Super Sleuth challenge

Beat the clock! You have 40 seconds to list all of the numbers you can think of between 732.1 and 732.2. Good luck!

**Today's Marks:** /6

# Day Four Try these.

CLUES

1. Write two puzzles for a partner using the numbers in the image. You can use decimal points in your puzzles.

(a)

(b)

Marks: /2

2. Would it take longer to (a) count to 10 in 0.1s or (b) count to 1 in 0.01s? Estimate which would take longer and then work it out with a partner.

Answer: Marks: /2

3. In the table below are the results from the under-14s freestyle 100 m race. (a) In the first row of boxes provided, round each number to three decimal places. (b) In the second row of boxes provided, rank the swimmers in order (1st, 2nd, 3rd and 4th) starting with the girl who swam the fastest.

| Antoinette | Louise | Margot | Eve |
|---|---|---|---|
| 61.7314 seconds | 61.7055 seconds | 61.7316 seconds | 61.7341 |
| | | | |
| | | | |

Marks: /8

4. In your copy, find out the following and write them in word and expanded form: (a) the number of pupils in your school, (b) the capacity of Croke Park, (c) the population of your county and (d) the population of Ireland.

Answers: (a) (b) (c) (d) Marks: /8

Today's Marks: /20

## Super Sleuth investigates

A famous mathematician named Alfred North Whitehead once said:

"The point about zero is that we do not need to use it in the operations of daily life. No one goes out to buy zero fish."

In groups or as a class, discuss this statement.
Do you agree or disagree? Give reasons for your answer.

Total Marks: /42 | I can identify place value in whole numbers and decimals. Yes  No

I can round decimal numbers to two or three decimal places. Yes No

# 3 Addition and Subtraction

**We are learning to:** Add and subtract whole numbers and decimals. ☐ Work backwards to solve puzzles. ☐

## Day One

**Study the steps used to solve the problem in the example below.**

Áine sold her house for €396,175. Prior to this, the value of the house had dropped by €75,000, but increased by €35,925 after Áine renovated it. How much did she pay for the house when she bought it originally?

**Circle the numbers and keywords:**
€396,175, dropped (decreased) by €75,000, increased by €35,925

**Link with operation needed (+, –, × or ÷):** Add (+). Subtract (–).

**Use a strategy:** Work backwards.

**Estimate and calculate:**

| My estimate: €435,175 | €396,175 + €75,000 = €471,175 (price before the value dropped)<br>€471,175 – €35,925 = €435,250 (value before renovation) | **Answer:** €435,250 |
|---|---|---|

**Summarise and check how you got your answer:**
I worked backwards to find the original price.

**Top tip:** Overall, the value dropped by around €39,000, so the original price was around €39,000 greater than €396,175.

### Try these.

CLUES

1. The number of bricks used to build a two-storey house was 82,300. The number of bricks used to build a bungalow was 53,500. How many bricks were used to build these two homes?

**Answer:** ______ **Marks:** __ /2

2. Last year, the average house price in Waterford was €174,900, while the average house price in Longford was €98,058. What was the difference between these average prices?

FOR SALE

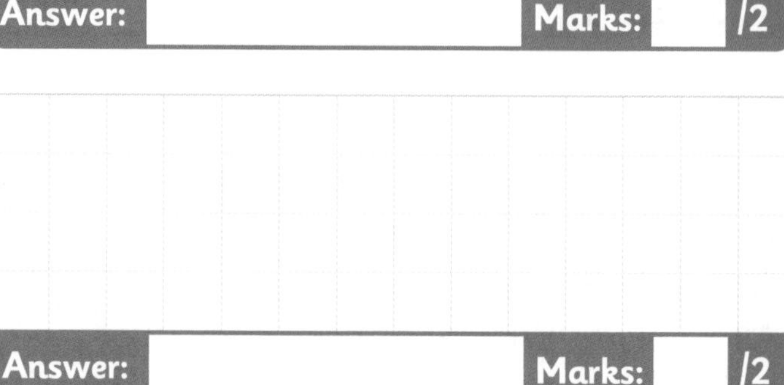

**Answer:** ______ **Marks:** __ /2

3. Suntown has three housing estates and a population of 125,301. If 56,864 people live in Sun Avenue and 48,299 people live in Sun Valley, how many people live in Sun Park?

**Answer:** ______ **Marks:** __ /2



**Today's Marks:** __ /6

# Day Two Try these.

*Galway's Got Talent* took place in the Town Hall last weekend and was broadcast online. There were four finalists.

1. **(a)** Fill in the missing values in the table below. **(b)** In the boxes provided, rank the contestants in order (1st, 2nd, 3rd and 4th), starting with the act that got the most votes.

| Contestants | Online Votes | Audience Votes | Backstage Votes | Phone Votes | Total Votes | Rank |
|---|---|---|---|---|---|---|
| **The Magic Master** | | 352 | 41 | 789 | **5,277** | |
| **Finbar and Oscar the Wonder Dog** | 9,412 | 407 | 35 | 1,204 | | |
| **The Claddagh Irish Dancers** | 5,810 | 244 | | 654 | **6,729** | |
| **Karate Kid Calvin** | 3,686 | 468 | 29 | 508 | | |

**Top tip:** Use the strategy of working backwards.

**Marks:** /8

2. How many votes were cast altogether?

**Answer:** **Marks:** /2

3. Find the difference between the online votes and phone votes.

**Answer:** **Marks:** /2

**Today's Marks:** /12

## Day Three Try these.

CLUES

Lara and her friends took part in an online gaming competition called Decimal Destroyers. They each played three rounds.

1 **(a)** Fill in the missing values in the table below. Estimate first.
**(b)** In the boxes provided, rank the girls in order (1st, 2nd and 3rd), starting with the highest score.

**Top tip:**
Use the strategy of working backwards.

| Participant | Round 1 | Round 2 | Round 3 | Total Score | Rank |
|---|---|---|---|---|---|
| **Lara** | 158.369 | 243.77 | 199.091 | | |
| **Magda** | 148.009 | 185.748 | | **572.407** | |
| **Olga** | 245.87 | | 174.524 | **599.4** | |

**Estimates of Missing Values**

| Lara | Magda | Olga |
|---|---|---|
| | | |

Marks: /6

2 Identify the round with the largest total score.

Answer: Marks: /2

3 What was the difference between the highest score and the lowest score achieved in the game?

Answer: Marks: /2



Today's Marks: /10

# Day Four Try these.

CLUES

## Puzzle power

In this pyramid puzzle, the value of each brick is found by adding the values of the two bricks below it. Can you complete the pyramid? Check your answers using a calculator.

| | | | |
|---|---|---|---|
| 246,395 | | | |
| | 169,125 | | |
| 45,261 | | | |
| | 14,110 | | |

## Super Sleuth challenge

Create a colour-by-number puzzle for a partner to solve. The puzzle has been started for you.

| **53,208 – 27,567 =** | **light blue** |
|---|---|
| | |
| | |
| | |
| | |
| | |

## Super Sleuth investigates

Make up three questions based on the information in the image. Swap them with another group and solve each other's questions.

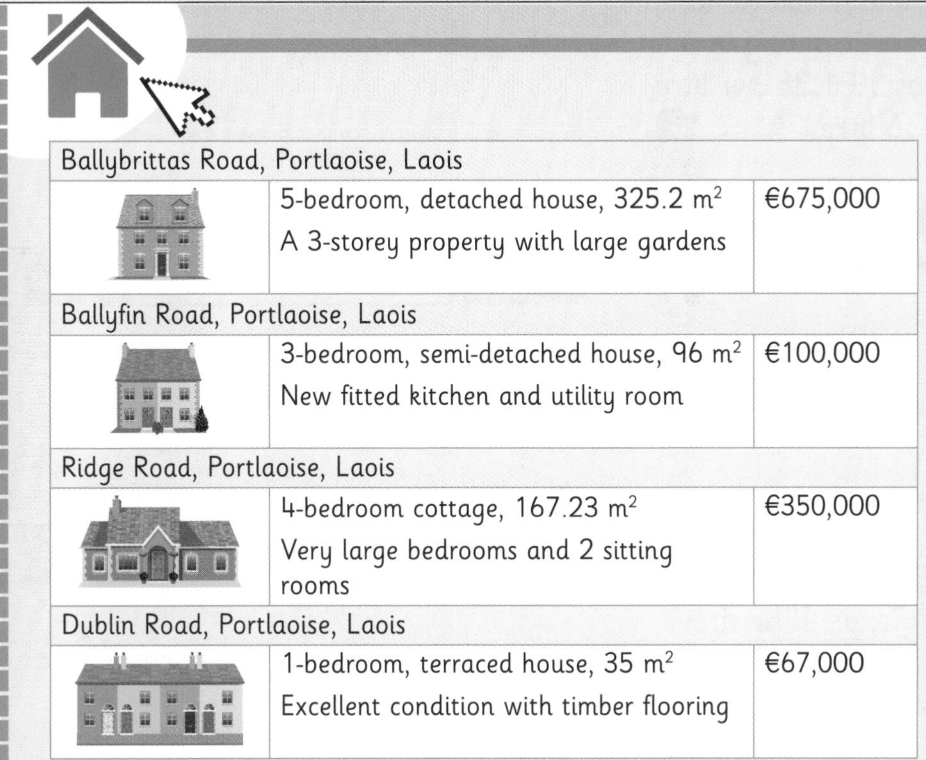

| Ballybrittas Road, Portlaoise, Laois | | |
|---|---|---|
| | 5-bedroom, detached house, 325.2 $m^2$<br>A 3-storey property with large gardens | €675,000 |
| **Ballyfin Road, Portlaoise, Laois** | | |
| | 3-bedroom, semi-detached house, 96 $m^2$<br>New fitted kitchen and utility room | €100,000 |
| **Ridge Road, Portlaoise, Laois** | | |
| | 4-bedroom cottage, 167.23 $m^2$<br>Very large bedrooms and 2 sitting rooms | €350,000 |
| **Dublin Road, Portlaoise, Laois** | | |
| | 1-bedroom, terraced house, 35 $m^2$<br>Excellent condition with timber flooring | €67,000 |

**Duties**

Reader
Calculator
Checker
Reporter

Total Marks: ____ /28 | I feel confident about ____

I would like to work on ____

Week 4

# 4 Multiplication and Division

**We are learning to:** Multiply a decimal by a decimal. ☐ Visualise to solve puzzles. ☐ Divide a decimal by a decimal. ☐

## Day One

**Study the steps used to solve the problem in the example below.**

If a steam engine can travel 19.75 km in 1 hour, how many kilometres could it travel in 3.5 hours?

**Circle the numbers and keywords:**
1 hour = 19.75 km, 3.5 hours = ? km

**Link with operation needed (+, –, × or ÷):** Multiply (×).

**Use a strategy:** Visualise.

**Estimate and calculate:**

| My estimate: less than 80 km | 19.75 km × 3.5 = 69.125 km | Answer: 69.125 km |
|---|---|---|

**Summarise and check how you got your answer:**
I drew 3 bars, each with 19.75 km and 1 bar with 9.875 km. I checked my answer by adding these four values.

**Top tip:**
Round the values to the nearest whole number when estimating:
19.75 km → **20 km**
3.5 → 4
**20 km** × 4 = **80 km**
Always compare your answer with your estimate.

### Try these.

CLUES

1. The Speed Machine needs to fill up his tank before participating in a race! If petrol costs €1.25 per litre, how much will 36 litres of petrol cost?

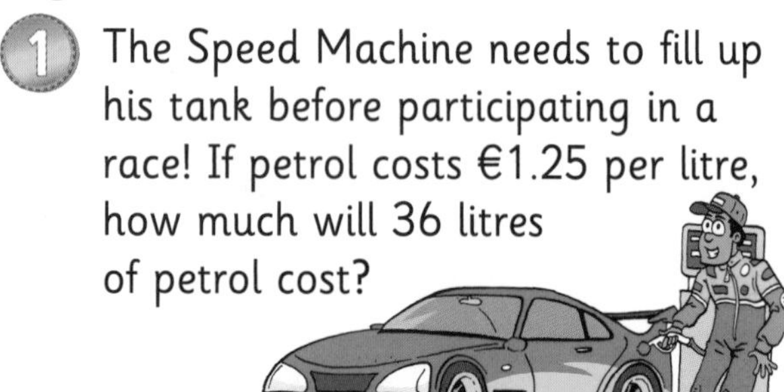

**Answer:** ______ **Marks:** ___ /2

2. The Speed Machine can travel 9.75 km using 1 l of petrol. How many kilometres could he travel using 25.5 l?

**Answer:** ______ **Marks:** ___ /2

3. The Speed Machine took a 28-day road trip across Texas. If he drove 2,086 km in total and drove the same distance each day, how many kilometres did he travel per day?

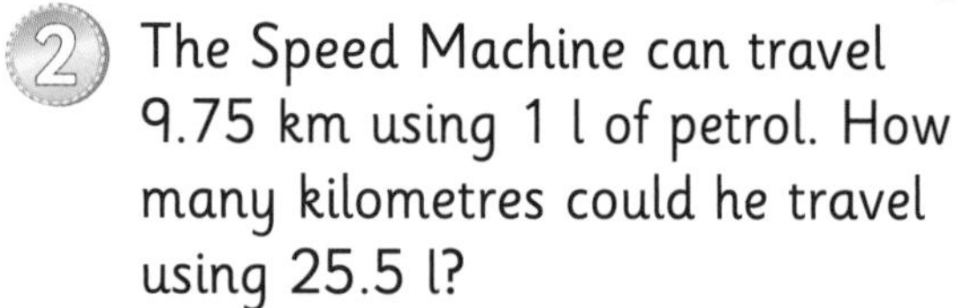

**Answer:** ______ **Marks:** ___ /2



**Today's Marks:** ___ /6

# Day Two Try these.

Super Sue asked her friend Baker Bob to make a chocolate biscuit cake for her birthday party. Baker Bob has offered to give Super Sue the cake as a gift, but only if she can work out how much the ingredients will cost!

| | Ingredients Needed | Cost | Total | |
|---|---|---|---|---|
| 1 | 0.227 kg butter | €2.96 per 0.454 kg | | |
| | 0.150 l golden syrup | €0.55 per 0.030 l | | |
| | 0.2 kg Maltesers | €12.40 per 1 kg | | |
| | 0.6 kg digestive biscuits | €1.09 per 0.1 kg | | Marks: /8 |
| 2 | 0.125 kg chocolate | €2.64 per 0.1 kg | | |
| | 0.125 kg almonds | €10.80 per 1 kg | | |
| | 0.125 kg cherries | €9.20 per 1 kg | | |
| | 0.4 kg rich tea biscuits | €0.67 per 0.1 kg | | Marks: /8 |
| 3 | Total cost of ingredients: | | | Marks: /2 |

Share your answer with your classmates. Explain how you worked with your partner to figure out the cost of each item. Listen to other suggestions from your classmates. You might learn something that could help you with other maths puzzles.

Today's Marks: /18

## Day Three Try these.

CLUES

1. A drama society in Clare put on a production of *Annie* at a local theatre. The rows of seats in the theatre were marked A–Z, with 43 seats in each row. How many seats were there in total?

Answer: Marks: /2

2. Miss Clery decided to bring her 29 pupils to the matinée performance of *Annie* and she asked Mrs Woods to join them. If an adult's ticket cost €35 and Miss Clery collected a total of €766 for the tickets, how much did a child's ticket cost?

Answer: Marks: /2

3. Silly Miss Clery forgot to add the service charge to the cost of the tickets! If the service charge per adult's ticket was €4.75 and the service charge per child's ticket was €3.40, what was the new amount that Miss Clery had to pay for the tickets?

Answer: Marks: /2

4. At the final performance of *Annie*, there was one empty seat in row A, two empty seats in row B, three empty seats in row C and so on until row Z. Every seat that was occupied had an adult sitting in it. If the full cost of an adult's ticket (including the service charge) had been reduced to €36, how much money was spent on tickets at the final performance?

Answer: Marks: /2

Today's Marks: /8

## Day Four Try these.

CLUES

You are the teacher today! Write suitable questions for your class that match the criteria outlined below.

1. Write a multiplication puzzle with the product **28.604**.

Answer:

Marks: /2

2. Write a division puzzle with the quotient **15.5**.

Answer:

Marks: /2

3. Write a maths story with the following answer: **The average of these numbers is 14.255**.

**Top tip:** To find the average, add the sets of numbers together and divide by the amount of sets that you added.

Answer:

Marks: /2

4. One of your pupils makes the statement shown. Can you explain to him why this is not always the case?



Answer:

Marks: /2

Today's Marks: /8

Total Marks: /40 I feel confident about problem-solving when

My teacher can help me by

# 5 Money

**We are learning to:** Explore value for money. ☐ Convert other currencies to euro and vice versa. ☐ Solve problems involving Value Added Tax (VAT). ☐

## Day One Try these.

Rob wants to take dance lessons and he is trying to decide between the following options:

- Ballet option – 6 lessons for €75
- Irish-dancing option – 8 lessons for €94

Which option offers the best value for money?

**Top tip:** Use the strategy of simplifying. Look at the hints below to help you break this down into steps.

Ballet option: €75 = 6 × €____ Irish dancing option: €94 = 8 × €____

I have identified the information that I need. How will I find the missing values?

**Answer:** ____ **Marks:** ____ /3

Len would like to get the iPhone 7. He is trying to work out which of the following options offers the best value for money over a two-year period:

- Credit option – Buy the phone for €695 and spend €10 per month on credit.
- Contract option – Sign a two-year contract agreeing to pay €25 per month for the first six months and then pay €39 per month.

**(a)** Which option should he choose and **(b)** how much money will he save?

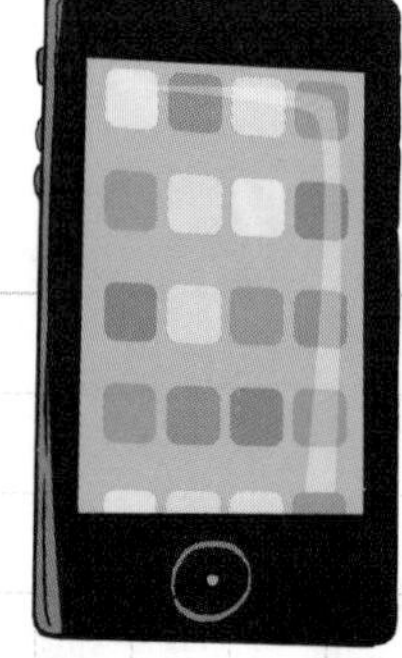

Credit option: | Contract option:

**Answers: (a)** ____ **(b) €** ____ **Marks:** ____ /3

3. Gemma won a sum of money in a raffle and went on a shopping spree. She bought a coat, a book and a bottle of perfume. The book cost €25 less than the perfume, which cost 0.2 of the price of the coat. After her shopping spree, Gemma had €33 left. If the book cost €15, how much did she win in the raffle?

**Answer:** ____ **Marks:** ____ /2



**Today's Marks:** ____ /8

## Day Two Try these.

**1** Find the total price of a hat that costs €50 plus 15% VAT.

Change the percentage to a fraction and simplify: $15\% = \frac{15}{100} = \frac{3}{20}$

Find $\frac{3}{20}$ of €50 = € ______ (VAT)

Finally, add € ______ (VAT) to €50 (original price) to find the total price.

**Answer: €** ______ **Marks:** /2

**Keywords**

**VAT** (Value Added Tax) is money that is collected by the government. They use it in the running of the country.

**2** Look at the menu. Find the total cost, including VAT, of a scone, a slice of carrot cake, an Americano and a soft drink.

**Answer: €** ______ **Marks:** /2

| A Latte Fun Coffee Shop Menu | |
|---|---|
| Americano | €2.75 plus 20% VAT |
| Café latte | €1.95 plus 20% VAT |
| Cappuccino | €2.20 plus 20% VAT |
| Mocha | €2.50 plus 20% VAT |
| Breakfast tea | €1.70 plus 20% VAT |
| Soft drink | €2 plus 20% VAT |
| Brownie | €1.20 plus 15% VAT |
| Scone | €1.60 plus 15% VAT |
| Muffin | €2.20 plus 15% VAT |
| Carrot cake | €2.40 plus 15% VAT |

**3** Order items from the menu above for you and your friend. Find the total cost of your bill including VAT. Check your answers using a calculator.

**Answer: €** ______ **Marks:** /2

**4** Harry Potty's Plumbing Services charged €240 to fix the coffee machine, including VAT of 20%. If the government increases the VAT to a rate of 22%, how much will this job cost, including VAT?

**Answer: €** ______ **Marks:** /2

**Today's Marks:** /8

## Day Three Try these.

This table shows examples of euro exchange rates. Use this information and the following rule to answer the questions below:

euro × exchange rate = foreign currency

**Example:** Helena bought a dress costing €35 online from a shop in New Zealand. How much did it cost in New Zealand dollars?

€35 × 1.66 = NZ$58.10

| Euro Exchange Rates | |
|---|---|
| British pound | £0.78 |
| American dollar | US$1.13 |
| Japanese yen | ¥125.76 |
| New Zealand dollar | NZ$1.66 |
| Indian rupee | ₹ 74.94 |

1. Kevin has €350 to spend during a holiday in California. How much is this worth in US dollars?

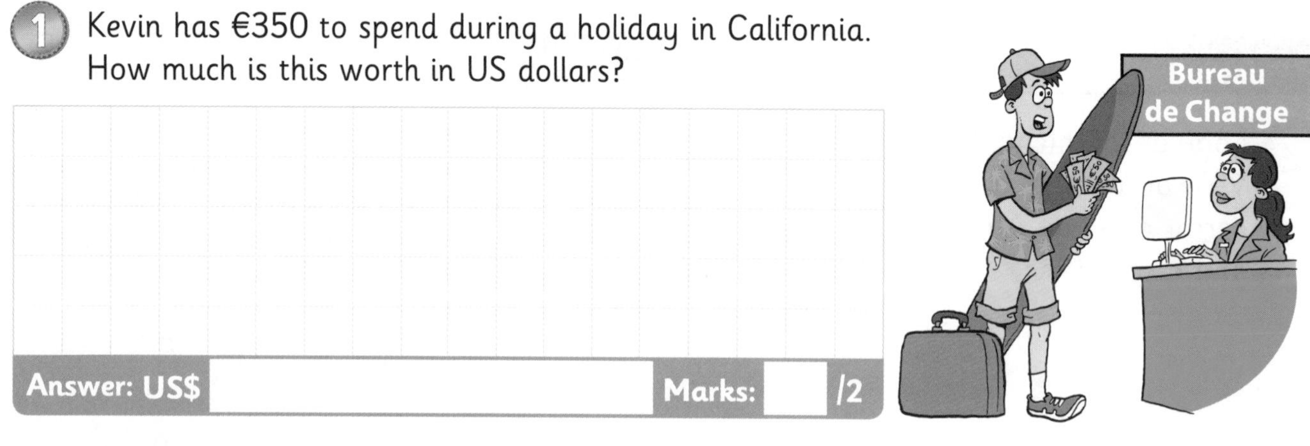


**Answer: US$** ______ **Marks:** ___ /2

2. Sunita is going to visit her relatives in India and plans to exchange €700 for spending money. How much will she get in Indian rupees?

**Answer: ₹** ______ **Marks:** ___ /2

3. **(a)** Mark has €250 to spend during a trip to Edinburgh. How much is this worth in British pounds? **(b)** If Mark has to pay 5% commission to the bank, how much money will he have in British pounds then?

**Keywords**

**Commission** is a fee charged by a bank for exchanging currencies.

**Answers: (a) £** ______ **(b) £** ______ **Marks:** ___ /4



**Today's Marks:** ___ /8

## Day Four Try these.

Use the table on page 26 and the following rule to answer the questions below:

foreign currency ÷ exchange rate = euro

1. Iseult is thinking of buying a computer game costing ¥6916.80 from a Japanese website. How much is this in euro?

**Top tip:**
Use a calculator to help you today.

Answer: € ______ Marks: ___ /2

2. Iseult has found an American website selling the same game for US$56.50. Which website is cheaper?

Answer: ______ Marks: ___ /2

3. If delivery from Japan costs ¥1886.4 and delivery from America costs US$28.25, from which website should Iseult order the game to get the best value for money?

Answer: ______ Marks: ___ /2

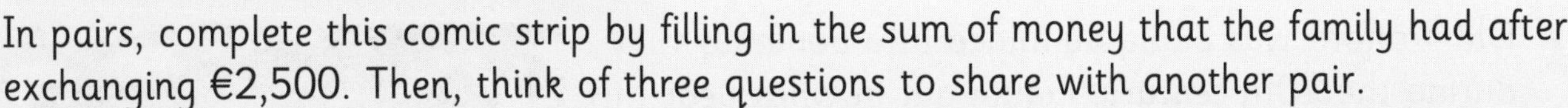

### Super Sleuth challenge

In pairs, complete this comic strip by filling in the sum of money that the family had after exchanging €2,500. Then, think of three questions to share with another pair.

Bureau de Change
5%
commission charge on all transactions

**Today's Marks: ___ /6**

Total Marks: ___ /30

I can answer a question about value for money. Yes ☐ No ☐

I can convert euro to a foreign currency and a foreign currency to euro. Yes ☐ No ☐

# 6 Revision 1

## Soccer Slam!

### Day One Try these.

1. The capacity of White Hart Lane, former home to Tottenham Hotspur, was 36,284. The club is building a new stadium with a capacity of 61,000. By how much will the capacity of its stadium increase?

Answer: Marks: /2

2. The capacity of Old Trafford is 14,635 greater than that of Tottenham Hotspur's new stadium. What is Old Trafford's capacity?

Answer: Marks: /2

3. Tickets for Tottenham Hotspur versus Arsenal were sold out when the two sides met in White Hart Lane for the final time. If 18,969 of the spectators were men and 11,547 were women, how many children attended the match?

Answer: Marks: /2

4. Old Trafford was badly damaged in a bombing during the 20th century. Figure out in what year this happened. The hundreds digit is 5 greater than the tens digit. The thousands digit has the same value as the units digit.

Answer: Marks: /2

### Puzzle power

Anna and Evan each received money for their birthday. Evan said, "Anna, give me €10 and I'll have as much money as you have!" Anna replied, "No chance! I want you to give me €10, so I'll have three times as much as you have." How much money did they each receive for their birthday?



**Strand:** Number **Strand Units:** Place Value; Operations – addition, subtraction, multiplication and division
**Strand:** Measures **Strand Unit:** Money

Today's Marks: /8

## Day Two Try these.

1. The Liverpool kit costs £49.50 for a man's kit, £37.50 for a woman's and £25 for a child's. What would the total price of one man's kit, one woman's kit and two children's kits be?

**Answer: £** ______ **Marks:** ___ /2

2. On Phil's first day working at Anfield, his job was to sell a meal deal with a programme for £13. If he took in £6,305, how many meal deals did he sell?

**Answer:** ______ **Marks:** ___ /2

3. Shamrock Rovers signed a new player on a very unusual 12-month contract. He will earn €1,100.25 per month for the first three months and for the next three months, this amount will be doubled. This pattern will continue until his contract is up. How much will he earn during his year at the club?

**Answer: €** ______ **Marks:** ___ /2

4. Shamrock Rovers will give a bonus to their new player if he scores more than 20 goals in his first season. The amount of money chosen for this bonus comes from the year in which the club was founded. Work out the amount he could receive.
   - The second digit is the fourth composite number.
   - When you divide the thousands digit into the units digit, the answer is 1.
   - If you multiply the tens digit by any other number, your answer will be 0.
   - The club was founded in the past 200 years.

**Answer: €** ______ **Marks:** ___ /2

**Today's Marks:** ___ /8

## Day Three Try these.

**1** This table shows the top five goalscorers in FIFA World Cup history. On average, how many goals did these players score in the FIFA World Cup?

| Player | Team | Goals |
|---|---|---|
| Miroslav Klose | Germany | 16 |
| Ronaldo | Brazil | 15 |
| Gerd Müller | Germany | 14 |
| Just Fontaine | France | 13 |
| Pelé | Brazil | 12 |

**Top tip:** To find the average, add the sets of goals together and divide by the amount of sets that you added.

**Answer:** **Marks:** /2

**2** **(a)** Manchester City's goalkeeper earns £110,000 per week. How much money does he earn over 52 weeks? **(b)** He has signed a four-year contract. How much will he earn altogether over the four years?

**Answers: (a) £** **(b) £** **Marks:** /2

**3** The captain of Manchester City Women's team earns £1,250 per week. How much more than this does the goalkeeper in question 2 earn per year?

**Answer: £** **Marks:** /2

**4** Using a calculator, work out how much **(a)** the player in question 2 and **(b)** the player in question 3 earns in euro per week. (To convert British pounds to euro, divide the amount by the exchange rate of 0.78, e.g. £1,250 ÷ 0.78.) Round your answers to two decimal places.

**Answers: (a) €** **(b) €** **Marks:** /2



**Today's Marks:** /8

# Day Four Try these.

**1** The Murphy family are going to Old Trafford to see a match. **(a)** Look at the image. How many children do Mr and Mrs Murphy have if they must pay £185 for one night's accommodation? **(b)** If they convert €650 to British pounds, how much will they get? (To convert euro to British pounds, multiply the amount by the exchange rate of 0.78.)

| Trafford Inn Room Rates |
|---|
| Adult: £65 per night |
| Child: £27.50 per night |

Answers: (a) ______ (b) £ ______ Marks: /4

**2** Can you figure out how many goals Cristiano Ronaldo scored for both Real Madrid and Portugal in a certain year using the clues below?

- It is a two-digit number.
- The number has eight factors.
- The number is less than 80.
- The units digit is twice the value of the tens digit.

Answer: ______ Marks: /2

**3** Write three interesting questions based on the image below and share them with your group. Examples: What fraction of the group are wearing red tops? What 2-D shape can you see on the footballs?

**Duties**

Question (a) ______

Question (b) ______

Question (c) ______

Today's Marks: /6

Total Marks: /30

# 7 Strategy: Visualising

## Day One

Drawing a diagram will help you to visualise a puzzle so that you can make connections and plan how to solve it. In this unit, you will get an opportunity to draw tree diagrams, timelines, pictures and Venn diagrams.

**Try these.**

CLUES

1. Granny Gormley has five children. Her eldest child has quadruplets, her youngest has triplets and each of her other children has twins. How many grandchildren does Granny have? Draw tree diagrams to show how many grandchildren there are. (One has been started for you.)

Eldest child

**Answer:** ______ **Marks:** ___ /2

2. For Granny's birthday this Friday, there will be 22 candles on each side of her square birthday cake. The number of candles on the cake will tell you what age Granny is. Draw a diagram of the candles on the cake. What age is Granny?

**Top tip:** The answer is not 88!

**Answer:** ______ **Marks:** ___ /2

3. Study all of the information below carefully and then fill in the details on Granny's timeline.

- Granny's first grandchild, Andrea, arrived when Francis was 25 years old.
- 7 years after Francis arrived, along came Granny's youngest child, Richard.
- Granny and Grandad's 50th wedding anniversary
- Granny was 5 years old when she started school.
- Granny was 21 when she married Grandad.
- Andrea started school when she was 4 years old.
- When Granny had been married for 3 years, her eldest child, Francis, was born.

| | | | | | | | | [This year] |
|---|---|---|---|---|---|---|---|---|
| ↓ | ↓ | ↓ | ↓ | ↓ | ↓ | ↓ | ↓ | |
| Granny born | | | | | | | | Birthday party |

**Marks:** ___ /8

**Today's Marks:** ___ /12

## Day Two Try these.

1. Granny's party will start at 4:35 pm and is due to end at 7:25 pm. For how long will the party last? Count on from 4:35 pm to 7:25 pm using the diagram below.

**Top tip:** Breaking up a puzzle in this way can make it much easier to solve.

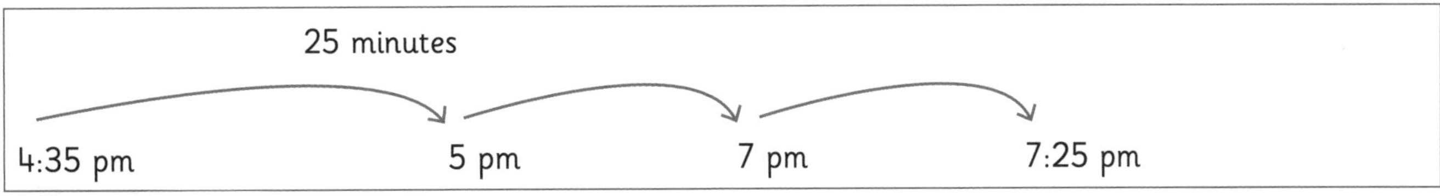


**Answer:** **Marks:** /2

2. Granny's son Richard was making wooden signs to help visitors find the house. He had to saw a length of wood into 9 sections. Each time he started, it took him 50 seconds to saw off another section. How long did it take him to saw the wood into 9 sections?

**Top tip:** Many people might think that you multiply 9 times 50 seconds, but you're too clever for that! Draw a diagram to help you with this.

**Answer:** **Marks:** /2

3. Granny's granddaughter Andrea was in charge of the invitations. She gave all of Granny's children and grandchildren two invitations each plus two extra for inviting friends. How many invitations did she give out?

**Top tip:** Draw a tree diagram.

**Answer:** **Marks:** /2

**Today's Marks:** /6

## Day Three Try these.

1. Granny's 4 eldest grandchildren decided to play one game of chess with each other. How many games of chess were played?

**Top tip:** Draw a tree diagram.

**Answer:** **Marks:** /2

2. Granny's other grandchildren enjoyed fun activities at the party. Label the circles in the Venn diagram and put in the information from the grid.

| | Horse riding | Face paints | Bouncy castle |
|---|---|---|---|
| **Ingrid** | ✓ | | ✓ |
| **Damien** | | ✓ | |
| **Cora** | | ✓ | ✓ |
| **Tomás** | ✓ | | |
| **Claire** | ✓ | ✓ | ✓ |

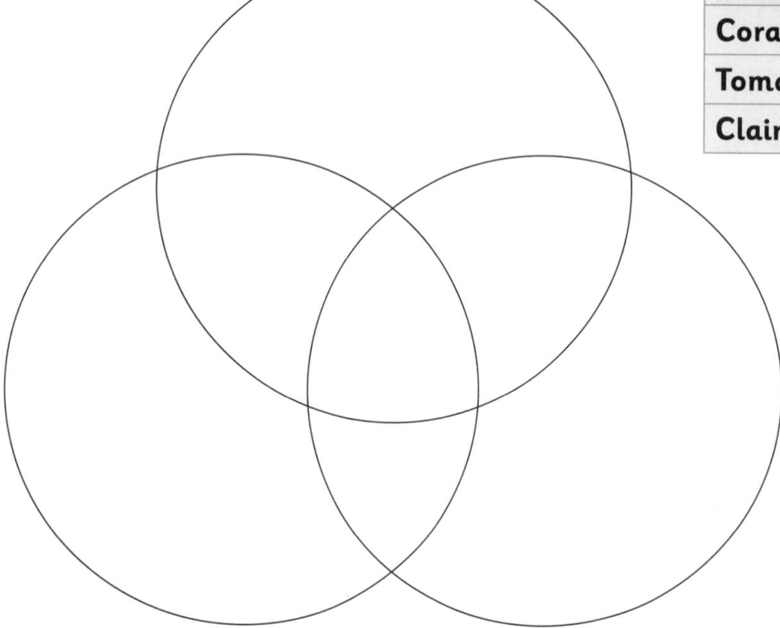

**Marks:** /2

3. Grandad loves puzzles. He arranged slices of birthday cake in a pattern as shown in image **A**. He asked Damien to only move neighbouring pairs of slices and make the arrangement look like image **B**. What was the fewest number of moves that Damien needed to make to complete the challenge?

**Top tip:** Act it out.

**Answer:** **Marks:** /2



**Today's Marks:** /6

# Day Four Try these.

1. Using a scale of 1 cm = 1 km, draw a map to Granny's house based on the following directions:
   - Starting at the traffic lights, travel 3 km north.
   - Turn right and travel 6.5 km until you reach a roundabout.
   - At the roundabout, take the third exit and travel 1.5 km and stop.
   - Label this spot as Granny's house.

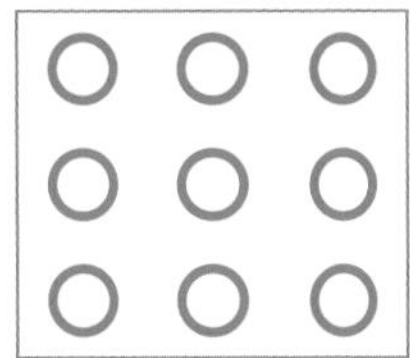


Marks: /2

2. A children's entertainer at the party baffled everyone with the following challenge: By drawing just 4 straight lines without lifting your pencil from the page, can **you** put a line through each of these 9 circles? Think outside the box for this puzzle!

Marks: /2

3. In Granny's garden, Cora was bouncing on the bouncy castle and Ingrid was lying on the ground. They could both see into a field in which there were lambs and geese. Cora could see only their heads, while Ingrid could see only their legs. If there were 35 heads and 82 legs, how many of each type of animal were there in the field?

Answer: Marks: /2

Today's Marks: /6

## Super Sleuth investigates

In groups, decide on a question with three possible answers that you will ask your classmates. Example: Do you like sport or music, or both? Record their responses on a tally sheet like the one below. Use the data to create a Venn diagram.

| Option 1: sport | |
|---|---|
| Option 2: music | |
| Option 3: reading | |
| All three | |

### Duties

Total Marks: /30 How do I choose what diagram to use in a maths puzzle?

What will I do if this diagram doesn't help me to solve the puzzle?

# 8 Equations and Variables

**We are learning to:** Use a letter to represent a variable in a number sentence. ☐
Translate word problems with a variable into number sentences. ☐

## Day One Study the steps used to solve the problem in the example below.

3 bars of chocolate weigh the same as 8 packets of sweets. If each packet of sweets weighs 33 g, how much does each bar of chocolate weigh?

**Circle the numbers and keywords:**
$3b = 8 \times 33$ g ('$b$' represents the bars of chocolate)

**Link with operation needed (+, –, × or ÷):** Multiply (×). Divide (÷).

**Use a strategy:** Visualise.

**Estimate and calculate:**
$3b = 264$ g $b = 88$ g **Answer:** 88 g

**Summarise and check how you got your answer:**
Each chocolate bar weighed 88 g. I multiplied 8 × 33 g to find the total weight of 8 packets of sweets. I then divided that number by 3 to find the weight of each bar of chocolate.

**Top tip:**
When we don't know the value of a number, we use a letter to represent the missing number.

**Try these.**

1. At Calypso's Crazy Circus, 6 children's tickets cost the same amount as 4 adults' tickets. If each child's ticket costs €5, how much does an adult's ticket cost?

**Answer:** **Marks:** /2

2. 16 unicycles weigh the same as 9 tandem bicycles. If a tandem bicycle weighs 32 kg, what is the weight of 1 unicycle?

**Answer:** **Marks:** /2

3. Aoife spent $\frac{3}{5}$ of her weekly pocket money buying a clown costume. If she spent €15 on the costume, how much pocket money does she get per week? (Hint: We know that Aoife only spent part of her pocket money. This means that your answer must be greater than €15.)

**Answer:** **Marks:** /2



**Today's Marks:** /6

## Day Two Try these.

1. Four pairs of 3-D glasses and 4 cinema tickets cost €40. If one pair of glasses costs €2, how much does each ticket cost?

Answer: Marks: /2

2. If the cost of 6 tacos is the same as that of 16 packets of Smarties, how much does each packet of Smarties cost?

One taco = €4
Smarties = €?

Answer: Marks: /2

3. Screen 1 in the cinema seats 210 people. If screen 1 was $66\frac{2}{3}$ % full and a ticket costs €9.90, how much money was made on cinema tickets that night?

Answer: Marks: /2

4. Audriana works in the shop at the cinema. One night, she added up a total of €2,432.50 in the tills. The shop had sold 240 popcorns at €6.25 each and 150 soft drinks at €2.75 each. If the rest of the money came from sales of a meal deal costing €8, how many meal deals were sold that night?

Answer: Marks: /2

€6.25

€2.75

€8

### Super Sleuth challenge

Fill in values in the boxes, making sure that each number sentence makes sense. Then, ask your teammates to work out the value of '$x$' in each number sentence.

$\square x + \square = \square$

$\square x - \square = \square$

### Duties

Reader

Calculator

Checker

Reporter

Today's Marks: /8

## Day Three Try these.

1. These are the top 6 bestselling apps in the app store:
   - Instasnapz (IZ) €1.49
   - Homework Helper (HH) €3.50
   - Music Maestro (MM) €1.10
   - Style Diaries (SD) €1.89
   - Coding Conundrums (CC) €0.99
   - Mindfulness for Teens (MT) €2.99

   Mum has given her 4 children a budget of €20 altogether to spend on apps. Work out how much each child wants to spend. Figure out if Mum's budget is enough pay for these apps.
   - Brian: MT + HH + CC
   - Seán: IZ + MM
   - Amy: SD + CC + MM
   - Cathal: HH + IZ

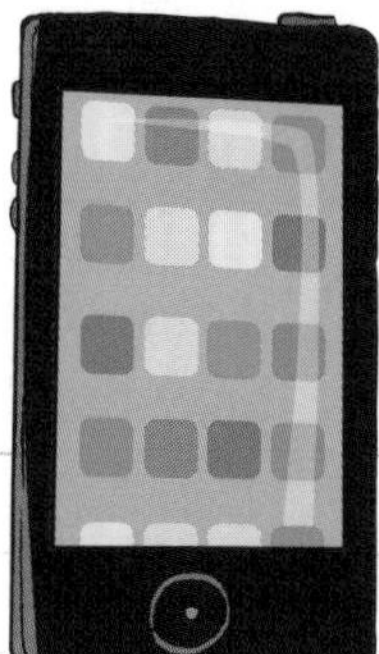

**Answer: Mum's budget will cover the cost of these apps with €____ to spare.**

Marks: __ /3

2. Using your knowledge from other maths topics, can you work out what the following letters represent?

   **(a)** d = 2r

   **(b)** a = l × w

   **(c)** v = l × w × h

Marks: __ /3

3. Now that Lexi is in 6th Class, she is spending quadruple the time on her homework plus an additional 10 minutes compared with the time that she spent when she was in Junior Infants. If she spends 1 hour and ten minutes on her homework now, how much time did she spend on her homework in Junior Infants? Write a number sentence to show your work.

**Answer:**

Marks: __ /2

### Super Sleuth challenge

Write three word problems inspired by the formulae in question 2 above.



Today's Marks: __ /8

## Day Four Try these.

1. Calculate the answers if $a = 4$, $b = \frac{1}{2}$ and $c = 2$.

(a) $a - b =$ (b) $(a \div c) + b =$ (c) $(c - b) \times a =$

Answers: (a) (b) (c) Marks: /6

2. Dev thinks of a number. He divides it by 5 and takes 458 from the answer. If he is left with 305, what number was he thinking of at the start?

**Top tip:** Work backwards and place the information that you have in a number sentence.

Answer: Marks: /2

3. In this game, each fruit represents a different value. When you add these values together, you get the answers for each row and column. **(a)** Find the value of each of the fruits using the information given in the grid. Remember to use a letter to represent the missing value. **(b)** Fill in the total for each column and row.

**Top tip:** Use logical reasoning.

| | | | | |
|---|---|---|---|---|
| apple | orange | banana | banana | 249 |
| grapes | banana | grapes | orange | |
| apple | apple | apple | apple | 184 |
| grapes | orange | orange | orange | 198 |
| 170 | | | | |

Answers: apple banana grapes orange Marks: /8

Today's Marks: /16

Total Marks: /38 The best part of my work in this unit was

I would like help with

# 9 Fractions

We are learning to: Add and subtract fractions. ☐ Multiply and divide fractions. ☐

## Day One Try these.

Write all fractions in their lowest terms.

1. In a long jump competition, the three attempts of each athlete must be added together and the longest total distance wins. Work out who the winner is below.

| Athlete | 1st Jump | 2nd Jump | 3rd Jump | Total Distance |
|---|---|---|---|---|
| Hopping Holly | $3\frac{1}{2}$ m | $2\frac{5}{6}$ m | $3\frac{3}{4}$ m | m |
| Leaping Lucie | $2\frac{7}{8}$ m | $3\frac{1}{4}$ m | $3\frac{1}{8}$ m | m |
| Jumping Jane | $4\frac{2}{3}$ m | $5\frac{5}{6}$ m | Fault | m |

Marks: /6

2. Some of the records from the shot putt competition have been lost. Can you help by filling in the blanks?

| Athlete | 1st Throw | 2nd Throw | Total Distance |
|---|---|---|---|
| Strong Steve | $9\frac{1}{6}$ m | m | $18\frac{5}{12}$ m |
| Powerful Pavel | $10\frac{3}{8}$ m | $9\frac{3}{4}$ m | m |
| Mighty Michael | m | $9\frac{2}{3}$ m | $19\frac{3}{5}$ m |

Marks: /6

3. Work out which athletes came 1st, 2nd and 3rd in the javelin throw and fill in the table below. The aim is to throw the javelin the farthest. (Hint: Change all of the values to decimals, as this will make it easier to compare the results.)

| John | Ray | Terence | Carl | Niall | Kevin | Sam | Ger |
|---|---|---|---|---|---|---|---|
| 20.25 m | $19\frac{1}{2}$ m | $\frac{85}{4}$ m | 19.45 m | $\frac{100}{4}$ m | $20\frac{1}{3}$ m | $\frac{112}{5}$ m | $21\frac{3}{5}$ m |
| | | | | | | | |

Marks: /6



Today's Marks: /18

# Day Two Try these.

CLUES



**Multiplying Fractions**

$$\frac{\text{Numerator}}{\text{Denominator}} \times \frac{\text{Numerator}}{\text{Denominator}}$$

**Dividing Fractions**

Step 1: Invert the second fraction. This means turn it upside down.

Step 2:

$$\frac{\text{Numerator}}{\text{Denominator}} \times \frac{\text{Numerator}}{\text{Denominator}}$$

1. Marie has a recipe for 12 fairy cakes. However, she only wants to bake 9 fairy cakes, which is $\frac{3}{4}$ of the amount in the recipe. Work out the weight of each ingredient needed to bake 9 fairy cakes.

| Ingredients for 12 fairy cakes | Ingredients for 9 fairy cakes |
|---|---|
| $\frac{1}{5}$ kg self-raising flour | kg self-raising flour |
| $\frac{1}{8}$ kg caster sugar | kg caster sugar |
| $\frac{1}{10}$ kg butter | kg butter |
| $\frac{1}{4}$ kg coconut flakes | kg coconut flakes |
| $\frac{3}{40}$ l raspberry icing | l raspberry icing |
| $\frac{1}{12}$ l vanilla buttercream icing | l vanilla buttercream icing |

Marks: /12

2. In a diluted orange drink, the ratio of orange cordial to water is 1:9. This means that $\frac{1}{10}$ of the liquid in this glass is cordial and $\frac{9}{10}$ is water. If Marie wants 2,500 ml of orange squash for a party, how much orange cordial will she need?

Answer: Marks: /2

3. Marie made fairy cakes for Carmel. Carmel wanted a ratio of 3:4:5 for plain to coconut to iced fairy cakes. If Marie made 28 coconut fairy cakes, how many fairy cakes did she make altogether?

Answer: Marks: /2

Today's Marks: /16

## Day Three

Try these.

1. Draw a number line in the box below. The starting point is 2 and the end point is $3\frac{1}{2}$. Here are the numbers to be placed on the number line:

| $\frac{5}{2}$ | $3\frac{1}{5}$ | $2\frac{3}{10}$ | $\frac{9}{3}$ | $2\frac{7}{10}$ |
|---|---|---|---|---|

Plan how you will construct the number line with a partner. 

Marks: /2

2. Why can't a bicycle stand up on its own? Crack the code to find out!

| A | B | C | D | E | F | G | H | I | J | K | L | M |
|---|---|---|---|---|---|---|---|---|---|---|---|---|
| $\frac{1}{5}$ | $\frac{4}{9}$ | $\frac{1}{3}$ | $1\frac{2}{5}$ | $\frac{3}{8}$ | $\frac{2}{15}$ | $1\frac{2}{3}$ | $\frac{9}{11}$ | $\frac{1}{2}$ | $\frac{7}{12}$ | $\frac{2}{55}$ | $1\frac{3}{4}$ | $\frac{11}{15}$ |

| N | O | P | Q | R | S | T | U | V | W | X | Y | Z |
|---|---|---|---|---|---|---|---|---|---|---|---|---|
| $2\frac{5}{11}$ | $\frac{17}{20}$ | $\frac{6}{13}$ | $\frac{5}{9}$ | $\frac{5}{8}$ | $\frac{8}{11}$ | $\frac{3}{7}$ | $\frac{4}{7}$ | $\frac{5}{6}$ | $1\frac{1}{4}$ | $\frac{1}{8}$ | $\frac{1}{100}$ | $\frac{13}{16}$ |

| $\frac{5}{7} \times \frac{7}{10} =$ | $\frac{10}{14} \times \frac{3}{5}$ | $\frac{1}{2} \div \frac{11}{16}$ | $1\frac{8}{35} - \frac{4}{5}$ | $\frac{3}{4} \div \frac{3}{5}$ |
|---|---|---|---|---|
| | | | | |
| | | | | |

| $\frac{1}{10} + \frac{3}{4}$ | $\frac{1}{7} \div \frac{1}{3}$ | $\frac{1}{20} \div \frac{5}{1}$ | $1\frac{1}{2} - \frac{7}{8}$ | $\frac{9}{10} \times \frac{5}{12}$ |
|---|---|---|---|---|
| | | | | |
| | | | | |

| $\frac{14}{15} \div \frac{2}{3}$ |
|---|
| |
| |

Answer:

Marks: /22

### Super Sleuth challenge

Create your own crack-the-code puzzle to share with your friends using the chart above.



Today's Marks: /24

## Day Four Try these.

CLUES

1. Little Ben has lost his favourite robot toy. Draw a 'missing' poster based on the following details:

- The robot's square head is $\frac{1}{3}$ the height of its body.
- Its two square brown eyes are $\frac{1}{4}$ the size of its head.
- Its two rectangular arms are $\frac{1}{2}$ the length of its body.
- Its two rectangular legs are $\frac{2}{3}$ the length of its body.
- It has a pink triangular nose and two triangular ears, which are $\frac{1}{3}$ the height of its head.
- It is otherwise grey in colour.

Compare your drawing with those of your classmates. Discuss the similarities and the differences.

2. $\frac{1}{3}$ of Ben's classmates were absent from school last week. Of the $\frac{1}{3}$ that were absent, $\frac{1}{2}$ of them went to the doctor. What fraction of Ben's class went to the doctor?

**Top tip:** Draw a diagram to help you visualise this puzzle.

**Answer:** **Marks:** /2

3. $\frac{8}{9}$ of Ben's classmates were at school for the Hallowe'en costume day. $\frac{1}{2}$ of those present dressed up as their favourite superhero. If 16 pupils dressed up as their favourite superhero, how many pupils are there in Ben's class altogether?

**Answer:** **Marks:** /2

**Today's Marks:** /4

### Super Sleuth challenge

In pairs, list all of the fractions you can think of that are less than $\frac{2}{3}$. You have only two minutes to complete this activity!

| **Total Marks:** /62 | **I can add and subtract fractions.** | Yes | No |
|---|---|---|---|
| **I can multiply and divide fractions.** | | Yes | No |

# 10 Decimals

**We are learning to:** Compare and order decimals. ☐ Round decimals to one decimal place. ☐ Add, subtract, multiply and divide decimals. ☐

## Day One

**Study the steps used to solve the problem in the example below.**

Rebecca cycled 15.05 km on Friday, half this distance on Saturday and 20.004 km on Sunday. What was the average distance that she cycled over the three days?

**Circle the numbers and keywords:**
15.05 km, half, 20.004 km, average

**Link with operation needed (+, –, × or ÷):** Add (+). Divide (÷).

**Use a strategy:** Simplify – break it into steps.

**Estimate and calculate:**

| My estimate: approximately 15 km | 15.05 km<br>7.525 km<br>+ 20.004 km<br>42.579 km | 42.579 km ÷ 3 = 14.193 km | **Answer:** 14.193 km |
|---|---|---|---|

**Summarise and check how you got your answer:**
I found the distances cycled, then added the three distances and divided by 3 to find the average.

**Top tip:** It is very important to keep the decimal point directly underneath the decimal point when adding and subtracting.

### Try these.

CLUES

1. Senan bought 0.6 kg of sweets, Sam bought 0.425 kg of sweets and Simon bought 0.09 kg of sweets. What was the total weight of the sweets that the boys bought?

Answer: ______ Marks: ___ /2

2. On Sunday morning, the owner of a sweet shop opened a new jar containing 2 kg of apple sours. By the end of the day, there was only 205 g left. What weight of apple sours had been sold? Write your answer in decimal form.

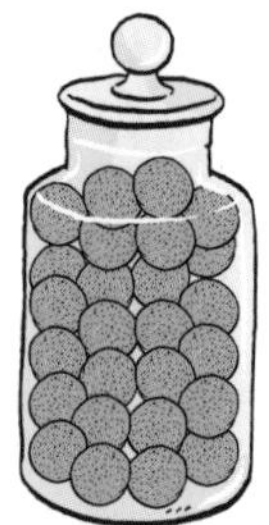

Answer: ______ Marks: ___ /2

3. Cola bottles cost €0.37 per 20 g. If Denise bought 460 g of cola bottles, how much money did she spend?

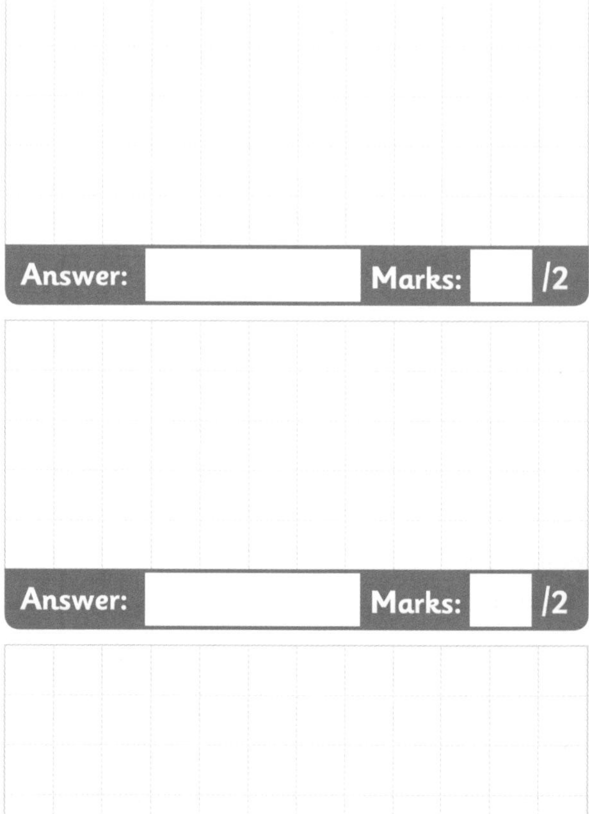

Answer: ______ Marks: ___ /2

**Top tip:** When multiplying decimals, remember to count back the correct number of decimal places.

Today's Marks: ___ /6

## Day Two Try these.

**Example:** Round 4.26 to one decimal place.

| 4.2 | 4.21 | 4.22 | 4.23 | 4.24 | 4.25 | **4.26** | 4.27 | 4.28 | 4.29 | 4.3 |
|---|---|---|---|---|---|---|---|---|---|---|

| | |
|---|---|
| **Underline the place.** | 4.26 |
| **Look at the neighbour to the right.** | We see the number 6. |
| **Remember the rounding rules.** | For 0 to 4, it stays the same forever more!<br>For 5 to 9, it moves one up the line! |
| **Make your decision.** | As the neighbour to the right is 6, this means that we must change 2 to 3. |
| **Everything to the left stays the same.** | **Answer:** 4.3 |

In groups of four, act out this activity using a die. Each pupil should roll the die once. Record the four numbers rolled in the following grid:

| **Numbers rolled:** | | | | |
|---|---|---|---|---|

Firstly, using the numbers rolled, write six numbers in the table below to three decimal places. Then, round each of your six numbers to two decimal places, one decimal place and the nearest whole number as shown in the example.

| **Example:** Our group rolled the numbers 4, 5, 1 and 6. | | | |
|---|---|---|---|
| Number to three decimal places: **1.456** | Nearest whole number: **1** | One decimal place: **1.5** | Two decimal places: **1.46** |

| Numbers to three decimal places: | 1 Two decimal places | 2 One decimal place | 3 Nearest whole number |
|---|---|---|---|
| (a) | | | |
| (b) | | | |
| (c) | | | |
| (d) | | | |
| (e) | | | |
| (f) | | | |

Today's Marks: /24

# Day Three

Try these.

**Target Board**

| | | | |
|---|---|---|---|
| 0.125 | 2.25 | 0.105 | 4.3 |
| 0.57 | 0.9 | 1.99 | 2.99 |
| 1.1 | 0.01 | 5.05 | 1.9 |
| 0.864 | 3.03 | 0.54 | 0.765 |

1. **(a)** Subtract the smallest number on the target board from the largest.
**(b)** Round the answer to the nearest whole number.

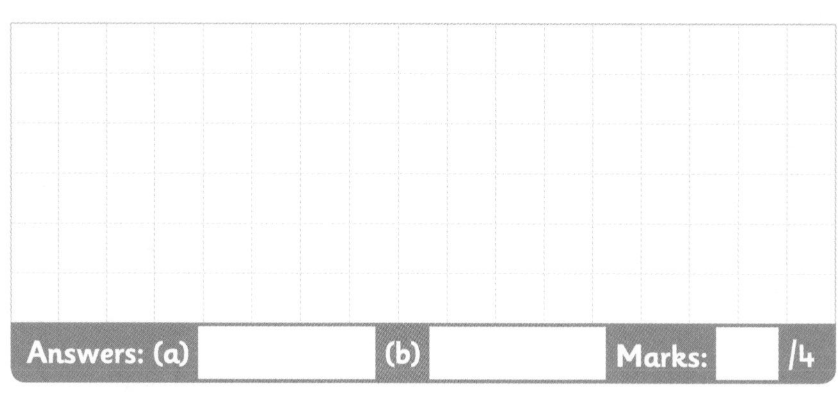

Answers: (a) (b) Marks: /4

2. **(a)** Add all of the numbers in the third row.
**(b)** Round the answer to one decimal place.

**Keywords**
**Rows** go across from side to side.

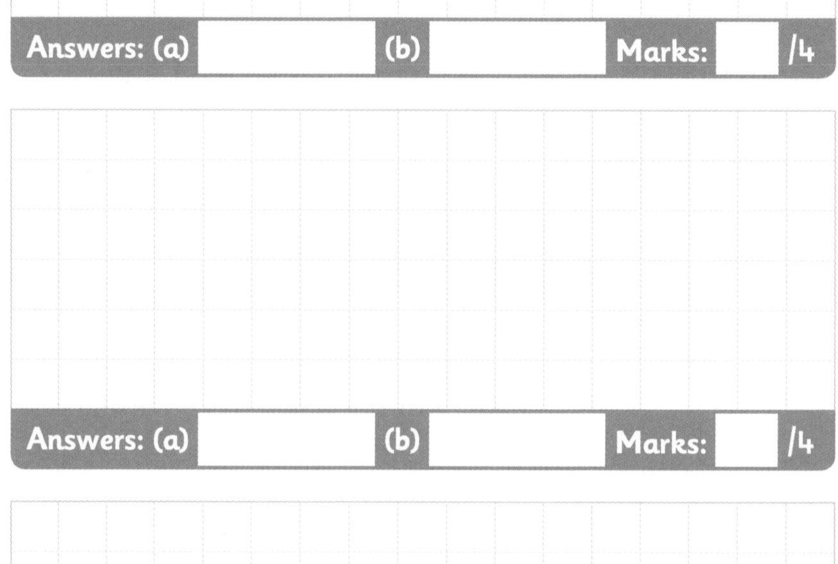

Answers: (a) (b) Marks: /4

3. **(a)** Add all of the numbers in the first column.
**(b)** Round the answer to two decimal places.

**Keywords**
**Columns** go up and down.

Answers: (a) (b) Marks: /4

4. **(a)** Multiply the two largest numbers on the target board.
**(b)** Round the answer to three decimal places.

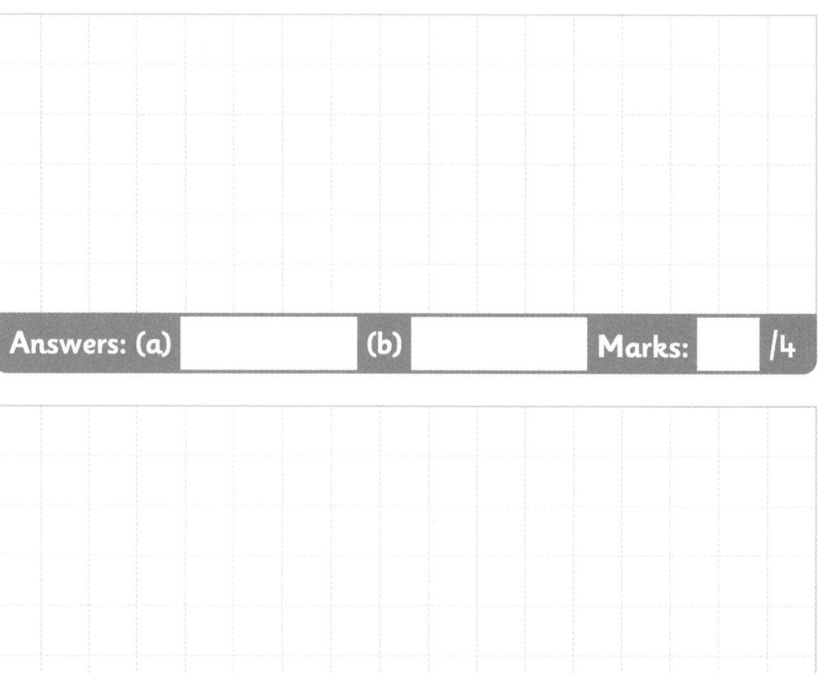

Answers: (a) (b) Marks: /4



Today's Marks: /16

# Day Four Try these.

1. 0.6 of the pupils in Tariq's school are girls. If there are 130 boys in Tariq's school, how many more girls than boys are there?

**Answer:** | **Marks:** /2

2. Tariq worked on a project about Italy. He spent 0.1 of his time printing photographs, 0.25 of his time completing the artwork and 0.15 of his time glueing pages into his scrapbook. He spent the remainder of his time typing. If Tariq spent 30 minutes on his artwork, how much time did he spend typing?

**Answer:** | **Marks:** /2

3. Tariq's teacher asked him to draw a diagram to illustrate that 0.01, 0.1 and 1 are all different numbers. Tariq doesn't know where to begin! Draw the diagram and describe the relationship between the three numbers to a partner.

**Marks:** /2

**Today's Marks:** /6

## Super Sleuth challenge

Use the target board on page 46 to create some fun puzzles to swap with a partner.

**Total Marks:** /52 | **One thing I found easy in this unit:**

**One thing I found difficult in this unit:**

# 11 Percentages

**We are learning to:** Calculate percentage profit or loss. ☐ Justify answers with explanations. ☐ Simplify by making numbers smaller. ☐

## Day One Try these.

You will need a calculator to check your work throughout this unit.

1. The cost of sending one child to the Gaeltacht is €925. For every other child from the same family, there is a 25% discount. What was the total cost of sending James and his brother Paul to the Gaeltacht?

Answer: € ______ Marks: /2

2. In their final exam, James got 28 out of 35 and Paul got 36 out of 40. **(a)** Work out which boy performed better. **(b)** Find the difference between the percentages that the boys received.

Answers: (a) ______ (b) ______ Marks: /2

3. While James and Paul were in the Gaeltacht, their parents bought a new car! The car had been reduced by 15% in a sale. If the original price of the car was €17,800, how much did their parents pay for it?

Answer: € ______ Marks: /2



Today's Marks: /6

## Day Two Try these.

Mr Callaghan organised a business fair with his class. Below are four of the businesses that were established.

**Keywords**

**Cost price** is the cost of making the item before profit is added. **Selling price** is the amount that the item is sold for.

| Top tip: Read every question before you start. | Kate's Homemade Lemonade | Peter's Second-hand Books | Seán's Chocolate Brownies | Bridget's Knitted Phone Covers |
|---|---|---|---|---|
| **Cost price** | €2.50 | €1.50 | €3.20 | €1.80 |
| **Selling price** | €3.00 | €2.50 | €2.80 | €2.40 |
| **Profit/loss** | € | € | € | € |
| **% profit/loss** | % | % | % | % |
| **New price** | € | € | € | € |

1. Calculate each pupil's money profit or loss per item sold. Fill in the table. Write the letter 'P' or 'L' next to the amount to indicate if they made a profit or a loss.

**Top tip:** Use a calculator for today's questions.

Marks: /4

2. Calculate each pupil's percentage profit or loss per item sold. Fill in the table.

Marks: /4

3. Towards the end of the fair, the pupils reduced their prices as follows: Kate by 10%, Peter by 20%, Seán by 15% and Bridget by 12.5%. What was the new price of each pupil's item? Fill in the table.

Marks: /4

Today's Marks: /12

## Day Three

Try these.

1. During the last Eurovision Song Contest, the cost of a phone vote was €1.80 including 25% VAT. How much did a phone vote cost before VAT was added?

Answer: Marks: /2

2. 55% of the countries that took part were represented by solo artists. If there were 18 bands in the contest, how many countries took part altogether?

Answer: Marks: /2

3. 15 of the countries that took part gave Denmark their top score. What percentage of the countries that took part was this?

Answer: Marks: /2

4. The Ukraine received 15% of the votes cast. If 4,686,867 people voted for the Ukraine, how many people voted altogether?

**Top tip:** The numbers in this question are very large. Use simpler numbers to think of how you would usually solve a puzzle like this.

Answer: Marks: /2



Today's Marks: /8

## Day Four Try these.

**1** While Paul was in the Gaeltacht, his school report card arrived at his house. How would you explain his results for Irish and maths to his parents?

**Paul's Report Card**
English: 5/8
Maths: 3/4
Geography: 7/10
History: 2/5
Science: 1/2
Irish: 10/30

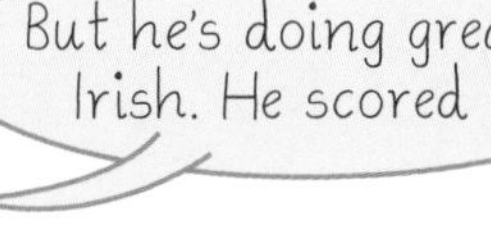


**Answer:**

**Marks:** /2

### Super Sleuth challenge

Create your own puzzles based on Paul's report card.

**2** List all the things that you know about 75%.

**Answer:**

**Marks:** /2

**3** Discuss the following statements with your group. Do you think they are accurate? Estimate what percentage of your life you spend doing homework and chores.

Work out what percentage of the past 7 days you have spent on the following:

| Activity | Time per day (on average) | Time per week | Percentage of the week |
|---|---|---|---|
| **Sleeping** | | | |
| **Eating** | | | |
| **In school** | | | |
| **Doing homework** | | | |
| **Doing chores** | | | |

**Top tip:** There are 168 hours in a week.

**Today's Marks:** /4

**Total Marks:** /30 **I felt that the work in this unit was**

**I would like my teacher to know that**

# 12 Revision 2

## Scoil na nÓg

## Day One Try these.

**Top tip:** When breaking down a puzzle, read the question fully first. Change the number stories into number sentences. Start solving them one by one.

1. Scoil na nÓg holds an annual sponsored walk. This year, it took the Junior Infants 40 minutes to complete the walk. It took the 6th Class pupils only 0.7 of this time to finish the walk. How long did it take the 6th Class pupils to reach the finish line?

**Answer:** **Marks:** /2

2. Mr Reilly's class raised €454 for the sponsored walk. Miss Coughlan's class raised $\frac{4}{5}$ of this amount, while Mr McDonnell's class raised 15% more than Mr Reilly's class. How much did the three classes raise altogether?

**Answer:** **Marks:** /2

3. After the walk, the pupils were treated to chocolate brownies. They were offered four options: (a) 13/6, (b) 1.75, (c) 200% or (d) $\frac{5}{2}$. Which option would you choose? Draw the four options to show how they compare.

| (a) | (b) | (c) | (d) |
|---|---|---|---|
| | | | |

**Answer:** **Marks:** /2

### Super Sleuth challenge

Design a set of loop cards with fractions, decimals and percentages for your class to play. Make sure your questions are challenging. Test your game with your class.



**Strand:** Number **Strand Units:** Fractions; Decimals; Percentages
**Strand:** Algebra **Strand Unit:** Equations and Variables

**Today's Marks:** /6

## Day Two Try these.

**1** The Parents' Association held a cake sale to raise money for the school concert. Work out how much money was raised using the following information:

- You could buy a cake for €4 or a bag of muffins for €6.
- $\frac{2}{9}$ of the families who attended bought a cake.
- 60% of the families who attended bought a bag of muffins.
- $\frac{5}{6}$ of the school's 324 families attended the cake sale.

**Top tip:** Work out how much money was spent on cakes first. Then, work out how much was spent on muffins, before finding out the total amount.

**Answer:** **Marks:** /2

**2** Miss Lawlor gave Tori some clues to help her work out the result of her maths exam. Tori thinks that she got 86%. Is she right? Change the sentences into number sentences to help you solve the puzzle.

- Tori's result was $\frac{17}{20}$ of what Simon got.
- Simon's result was double what Jessica got.
- Jessica received 0.666 of Torben's grade.
- Torben received 75%.

**Answer:** **Marks:** /2

**3** Miss Lawlor's class plays a maths game called Rock 'n' Roll. They roll a ten-sided die twice and use the numbers rolled to make a fraction. Then, they write each fraction as a decimal number rounded to three decimal places and as a percentage to the nearest whole number. Fill in the missing values for this game of Rock 'n' Roll. Try it yourself with your own die.

| Fraction | Decimal | Percentage |
|---|---|---|
| $\frac{1}{9}$ | | % |
| $\frac{5}{6}$ | | % |
| $\frac{2}{7}$ | | % |

**Marks:** /6

**Today's Marks:** /10

# Day Three

Try these.

CLUES

1. Scoil na nÓg has been busy preparing for the school concert. New curtains were bought for the stage. They were priced at €2,750, but the school received a discount of $\frac{1}{8}$ off the price. How much did the school pay for the curtains?

Answer: Marks: /2

2. How much did it cost for a family of two adults, two senior citizens and two children to see the concert?

**Ticket Prices**
Adult: €7.50
Child: €2.50
Senior citizen: €5
Special discount:
25% off when you buy six tickets or more

Answer: Marks: /2

3. $\frac{2}{5}$ of the duration of the concert was taken up with songs, 0.375 was taken up with dancing and the remainder was taken up with acting. If the concert was 1 hour and 20 minutes long, what length of time was taken up with acting?

**Top tip:** Before changing these sentences into number sentences, convert the decimal number to a fraction.

Answer: Marks: /2

4. Granny bought 5 raffle tickets and 8 chocolate bars for €23.30. If 3 bars cost €4.05, how much did each raffle ticket cost?

Answer: Marks: /2



Today's Marks: /8

# Day Four Try these.

| 1.00 = | 1 whole = | | 0.375 = | = | $37\frac{1}{2}$ % |
|---|---|---|---|---|---|
| 0.875 = | = | $87\frac{1}{2}$ % | 0.333 = | $\frac{1}{3}$ = | % |
| = | $\frac{2}{3}$ = | $66\frac{2}{3}$ % | = | $\frac{1}{8}$ = | 12.5% |
| 0.625 = | $\frac{5}{8}$ = | % | 0.25 = | $\frac{1}{4}$ = | % |
| 0.5 = | = | 50% | 0.2 = | = | 20% |

1. Work out and fill in the missing values in the chart above.

**Marks:** /10

2. Scoil na nÓg is $\frac{2}{9}$ the height of the local church. If Scoil na nÓg is 6.75 m high, what is the height of the church? **(a)** Place this information into a number sentence using a letter to represent the missing value. **(b)** Write your answer to two decimal places.

**Answers: (a)** **(b)** **Marks:** /4

3. The principal of Scoil na nÓg is 4 times older than Hannah. Scoil na nÓg is 102 years older than the principal. If Scoil na nÓg is 150 years old, how old is Hannah? Place this information in number sentences using a letter to represent the missing value.

**Answer:** **Marks:** /2

**Today's Marks:** /16

## Super Sleuth investigates

Twins Gina and Tina are having a dispute. Help them get to the bottom of it!

In your face, Tina! I got 0.6 of the test correct. Yay me!

I got $\frac{5}{8}$ of the test correct. Yay me!

Draw a diagram showing which result you believe is better and write a short explanation to the two girls.

# 13 Strategy: Trial and Improvement

## Day One

When you are not given the exact information that you need to start solving a puzzle, you might need to make an estimate. Once you have placed your estimate into the puzzle, check if it makes sense. If not, try again! If your estimate was too high, try a lower number. If it was too low, try a higher number.

**Try these.**

CLUES

1. Hayley bought 7 items made up of vases and paintings for her house. The vases cost €45 each and the paintings cost €99 each. She spent €477 in total. How many of each item did she buy?

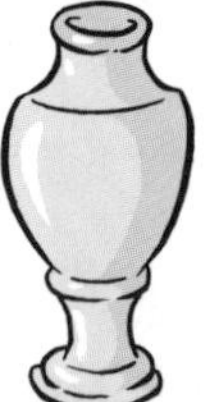

| Attempt | Vases | Paintings | Spent | Attempt | Vases | Paintings | Spent |
|---|---|---|---|---|---|---|---|
| 1 | | | | 2 | | | |
| 3 | | | | 4 | | | |
| 5 | | | | 6 | | | |
| 7 | | | | 8 | | | |
| 9 | | | | 10 | | | |

**Answer:** Marks: /2

2. The perimeter of Hayley's kitchen is 16 m. The length of her kitchen is 2 m longer than the width. Work out the length and the width.

| Attempt | Length | Width | Perimeter | Attempt | Length | Width | Perimeter |
|---|---|---|---|---|---|---|---|
| 1 | | | 16 m | 2 | | | 16 m |
| 3 | | | 16 m | 4 | | | 16 m |

**Answer:** Marks: /2

3. In Hayley's neighbour's field, there were hens and lambs. Hayley could see 66 heads and 186 legs in the field. How many lambs and hens were there?

| Attempt | Lambs | Hens | Heads | Legs | Attempt | Lambs | Hens | Heads | Legs |
|---|---|---|---|---|---|---|---|---|---|
| 1 | | | | | 2 | | | | |
| 3 | | | | | 4 | | | | |
| 5 | | | | | 6 | | | | |
| 7 | | | | | 8 | | | | |
| 9 | | | | | 10 | | | | |

**Answer:** Marks: /2



**Today's Marks:** /6

## Day Two Try these.

1. There are 130 nurses and vets working at the Animal Kingdom Veterinary Hospital. There are 50 more nurses than vets. How many nurses are there?

| Attempt | Nurses | Vets | Total Staff |
|---|---|---|---|
| 1 | | | 130 |
| 2 | | | 130 |

**Answer:** ______ **Marks:** ___ /2

2. There are only dogs and birds in Waiting Room A. Can you figure out how many dogs and birds there are if there are 32 legs and 10 heads? Two of the dogs have only 3 legs each.

| Attempt | Dogs | Birds | Total Heads | Total Legs |
|---|---|---|---|---|
| 1 | | | 10 | 32 |
| 2 | | | 10 | 32 |

**Answer:** ______ **Marks:** ___ /2

3. Maddie dropped her cat into the veterinary hospital for a check-up while her three cousins waited outside. Maddie is 1 year younger than Steve, but 2 years older than Kerry. Kerry is 4 years younger than Jamie. If their combined age is 53, how old is each person?

**Answers:** **Maddie** ___ **Steve** ___ **Kerry** ___ **Jamie** ___ **Marks:** ___ /4

4. After their trip to the veterinary hospital, Maddie and her cousins went shopping. Maddie spent twice as much as Steve, but €10 less than Kerry. Jamie spent €1 less than Steve. If they spent a combined total of €90, how much did each person spend? (Hint: Maddie spent an odd amount of money between €20 and €30.)

**Answers:** **Maddie** ___ **Steve** ___ **Kerry** ___ **Jamie** ___ **Marks:** ___ /4

**Today's Marks:** ___ /12

## Day Three

**Try these.**

You can use a calculator for today's puzzles. You might also work in groups.

1. 2,070 is the product of two consecutive numbers. Find out what these two numbers are. Plan your strategy first.

**Answer:** ______ × ______ = 2,070 **Marks:** /2

2. 80,940 is the product of two consecutive numbers. Find out what these two numbers are.

**Answer:** ______ × ______ = 80,940 **Marks:** /2

3. Organise Billy, Molly, Lily, Gillian and Polly's seating arrangements so that they will all be happy with their seats.

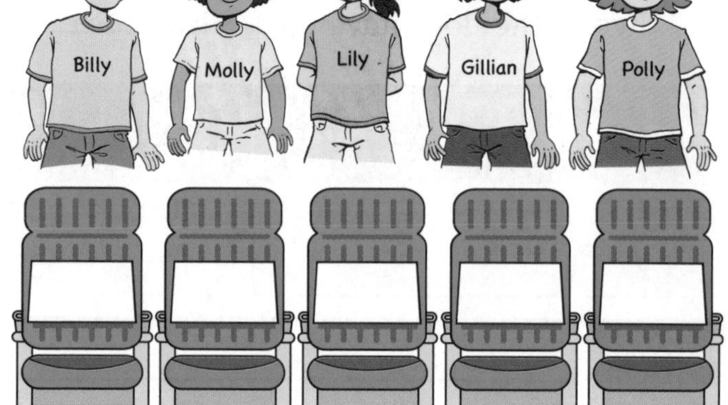


- Lily and Gillian are sharing popcorn and must sit together.
- Billy hates listening to Gillian munching her popcorn, so he wants to sit away from her.
- Molly wants to sit next to Lily, but away from Gillian, as they have had a tiff.
- Gillian sits on the far right.
- Polly arrives unexpectedly at the cinema and insists on sitting next to Billy, but away from the girls.

**Marks:** /2

### Puzzle power

Insert each of the digits 1 to 9 once to ensure that each side adds up to the same number.

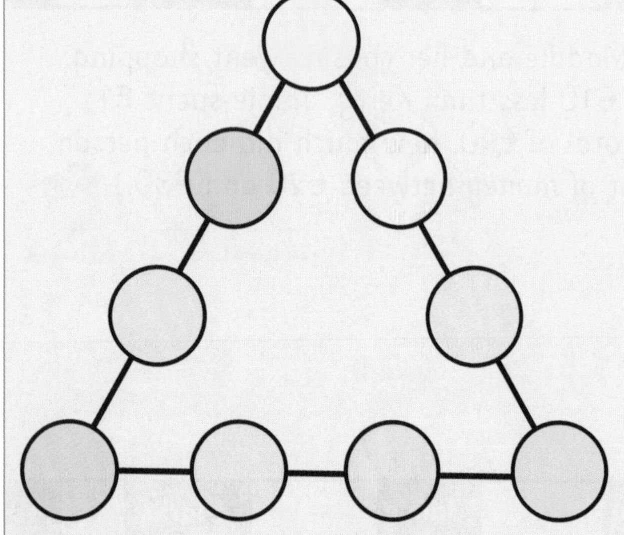

### Super Sleuth investigates

Place the following sums of money into the two purses, ensuring that there is an equal amount of money in each: 10c, 20c, 30c, 40c, 50c, 60c, 70c, 80c, 90c, €1, €1.10, €1.20.

**Today's Marks:** /6

# Day Four Try these.

CLUES

1. Ned Sheeran, Taylor Fast and Dustin Bieber entered a talent contest. Taylor scored 10 more points than Ned and 20 more points than Dustin. If their combined score was 255 points, how many points did each contestant score?

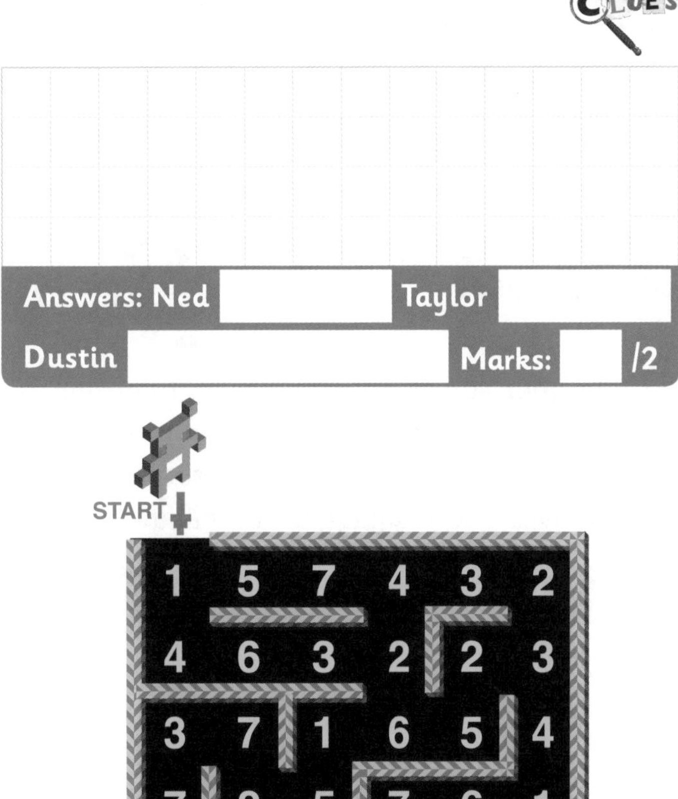


Answers: Ned ______ Taylor ______

Dustin ______ Marks: ___ /2

2. Travel through the maze and find **(a)** a path that adds up to 98, **(b)** a path that adds up to a prime number and **(c)** a path that adds up to a multiple of 3.

> **Top tip:**
> Trial and improvement requires patience. If you find a task too challenging, move onto another and return to it at a later time.

Marks: ___ /6

3. Three pupils in Miss Young's class are playing with headbands. They all have a two-digit number card on their headband. However, each child can only see the other two children's numbers. Use Miss Young's clues below to help each child work out their number and write it on their card. Miss Young tells them:

- "Levi and Mason, when I add your numbers and divide the answer by 3, I get 17.
- Charlotte and Levi, your numbers have a difference of 1. Also, when I add them together, I get a square number less than 30.
- Charlotte, your number would divide evenly into Mason's number 3 times.
- When I add up all three of your numbers, I get 64."

Marks: ___ /6

Today's Marks: ___ /14

Total Marks: ___ /38 | I remained focused on the tasks. Yes ☐ No ☐

I used maths language in my discussions. Yes ☐ No ☐

# 14 2-D Shapes

**We are learning to:** Construct triangles from given sides or angles. ☐ Construct circles. ☐ Tessellate combinations of 2-D shapes. ☐ Plot simple co-ordinates. ☐

## Day One Try these.

You will need a protractor, a ruler and a compass for this unit.

1. In your copy, use your pencil, ruler and compass to draw a pig with the measurements shown in the table below. Add isosceles triangles with two sides measuring 1 cm for the ears, as well as hooves and a squiggly tail. Fill in the missing values in the table.

Circumference
Radius
Centre
Diameter
Circle

| Body Part | Radius | Diameter |
|---|---|---|
| Head | 2.5 cm | |
| Body | 4.5 cm | |
| Snout | | 1 cm |
| Two nostrils | | 0.3 cm |
| Two eyes | | 0.5 cm |

Marks: /2

2. Write a definition of the word 'tessellation'.

**Answer:**

Marks: /2

3. Draw a tessellating pattern **(a)** using just one 2-D shape, **(b)** using equilateral triangles and hexagons and **(c)** using three different 2-D shapes.

**Top tip:**
Act out these challenges with 2-D shapes before you begin to draw.

| (a) | (b) | (c) |
|---|---|---|
| | | |

Marks: /6

### Super Sleuth challenge

Write instructions for a partner to construct another animal made up of circles using their compass. Swap and try to guess each other's animals.



Today's Marks: /10

## Day Two Try these.

CLUES

1. You have been tasked with designing a Formula 1 racing car for the new season. Include at least six different 2-D shapes in your design and use tessellating shapes for one part of the car.

**Top tip:**
When drawing straight lines in maths, always use a ruler.

Marks: /6

2. In your copy, draw three different scalene triangles, each with a perimeter of 30 cm.

Marks: /6

3. Draw **(a)** a triangle with one side measuring 5.5 cm, another side measuring 4 cm and one angle measuring 60° and **(b)** a right-angle triangle with one angle measuring 35° and one side measuring 3 cm.

| (a) | (b) |
|---|---|
| | |

Marks: /2

### Super Sleuth investigates

Super Sleuth has heard reports of a rival detective stating, "All 2-D shapes with straight lines are suitable for creating tessellations." Draw diagrams to prove whether this statement is true or false. Explain your diagrams to a partner.

Today's Marks: /14

## Day Three Try these.

CLUES

1. (a) Draw a rhombus and a regular trapezium in the boxes below.

| Rhombus | Regular trapezium |
| --- | --- |
| | |

(b) The similarities between a rhombus and a regular trapezium are:

(c) The differences between a rhombus and a regular trapezium are:

Marks: /4

2. An announcement has just been made that either the rhombus or the regular trapezium will become extinct in the next 24 hours! Which of these two shapes would you choose to save? Explain your answer.

Answer:

Marks: /2

3. Draw an item from your classroom with **(a)** 1 line of symmetry, **(b)** 2 lines of symmetry and **(c)** no lines of symmetry.

| (a) | (b) | (c) |
| --- | --- | --- |
| | | |

Marks: /6



Today's Marks: /12

# Day Four Try these.

1. Super Sleuth overheard a pupil say, "All 3-D shapes are made up of 2-D shapes." Is this statement true or false? Draw diagrams below to prove your answer.

Answer: Marks: /2

2. This grid contains 25 letters of the alphabet. Work out what word each set of co-ordinates below spells.

| 5 | V | C | F | O | W |
|---|---|---|---|---|---|
| 4 | L | A | R | J | Q |
| 3 | G | T | E | M | U |
| 2 | S | N | H | I | D |
| 1 | P | B | K | Y | X |
| | 1 | 2 | 3 | 4 | 5 |

**Top tip:**

A baby crawls   before they stand . Always move across the grid before moving upwards.

**(a)** (1, 2), (5, 3), (1, 1), (3, 3), (3, 4)

**(b)** (5, 2), (3, 3), (2, 3), (3, 3), (2, 5), (2, 3), (4, 2), (1, 5), (3, 3)

**(c)** (4, 2), (2, 2), (1, 5), (3, 3), (1, 2), (2, 3), (4, 2), (1, 3), (2, 4), (2, 3), (4, 2), (4, 5), (2, 2)

Answers: (a) (b) (c) Marks: /6

3. Use the grid above to create three messages of your own with co-ordinates. Share them with your classmates.

(a)

(b)

(c)

Marks: /6

Today's Marks: /14

## Super Sleuth investigates

1. What letters can you create using a tangram set?
2. What animals can you create using a tangram set?
3. Create three pictures using all seven shapes in a tangram set. Draw the outline of your pictures and give them to another pair to work out what they are.

Total Marks: /50 | I like/dislike working on 2-D shapes, because

It is important to learn about 2-D shapes, because

# 15 Length

**We are learning to:** Rename measures of length. ☐ Complete investigations involving the perimeter of regular and irregular shapes. ☐ Use and interpret scales on plans. ☐

## Day One

**Study the steps used to solve the problem in the example below.**

Sarah cycled 12 km in 45 minutes. How far could she cycle in 2 hours if she maintained the same speed throughout?

**Top tip:**
Sarah can cycle more than 12 km in one hour. I doubled this to find my estimate.

**Circle the numbers and keywords:** 12 km, 45 minutes, 2 hours

**Link with operation needed (+, −, × or ÷):** ÷, ×, +.

**Use a strategy:** Visualise. This bar model represents 1 hour:

1 hour

| 4 km | 4 km | 4 km | |
|---|---|---|---|

**Estimate and calculate:**

| My estimate: over 24 km | $\frac{3}{4}$ of an hour = 12 km<br>1 hour = 16 km | **Answer:** 32 km |
|---|---|---|

**Summarise and check how you got your answer:**
I worked out how far Sarah could cycle in 1 full hour. I doubled this to find the distance that she could cycle in 2 hours.

### Try these.

1. If Olivia can run 2 km 500 m in 40 minutes, how far could she run in 1 hour and 40 minutes?

**Answer:** ______ **Marks:** /2

2. Olivia's friend Shane can run 3.6 km in one hour. What is the difference between how far he and Olivia run in 1 hour and 40 minutes?

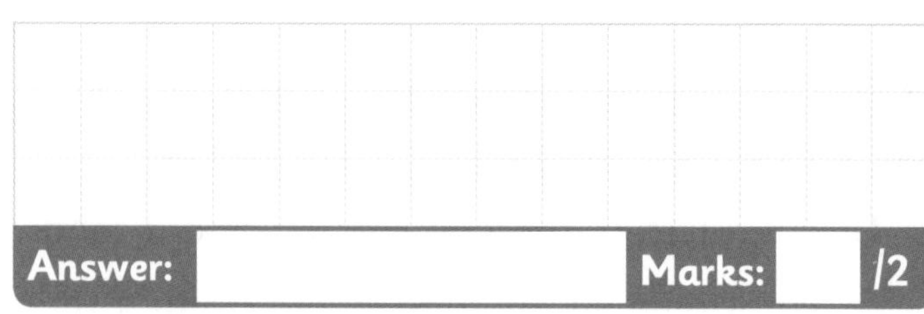

**Answer:** ______ **Marks:** /2

3. Zach and Fred ran a combined distance of 285 m in one minute. The difference between the distances that they ran was 11 m. If Zach ran farther, what distance did each boy run?

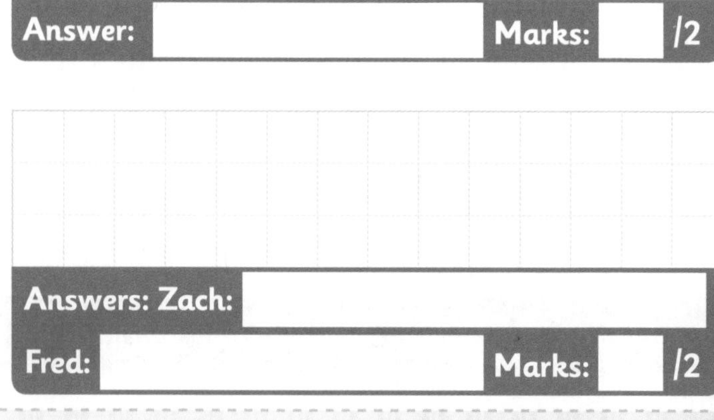

**Answers: Zach:** ______
**Fred:** ______ **Marks:** /2



**Today's Marks:** /6

## Day Two Try these.

CLUES

1. The average length of a basketball court is 29 m. What is the length of 14 courts?

Answer: Marks: /2

2. Rory runs an average of 4 $\frac{1}{10}$ km during a full basketball game. He played four games. He was taken off after one quarter in one game, two quarters in another, three quarters in another and he played one full game. How far did he run in these four games?

Answer: Marks: /2

3. Rory's family were travelling to Fota Island Wildlife Park on their holidays. Rory's uncle drove at an average speed of 87 km per hour for the first hour and a half of the trip, and an average speed of 95 km per hour for the next two hours. What distance did Rory's family travel to reach Fota Island Wildlife Park?

Answer: Marks: /2

Ask permission from your teacher or a parent to use Google Maps to investigate what area of the country Rory's family might have travelled from.

4. The tallest animal that Rory saw in Fota Island Wildlife Park was a giraffe. The smallest animal that he saw was a meerkat, which was $\frac{1}{16}$ the height of the giraffe. His favourite animal was the red panda, which, at 120 cm, was 4 times longer than the height of the meerkat. What was the height of the giraffe?

Answer: Marks: /2

Today's Marks: /8

## Day Three Try these.

CLUES

1. Draw a regular octagon with a perimeter of 16 cm.

Marks: /2

2. Draw an irregular hexagon with a perimeter of 36 cm.

Marks: /2

3. Draw an isosceles triangle with a perimeter of 20 cm. Label the measurements on each side.

**Keywords**

The **perimeter** of a shape is the sum of the length of its sides.

Marks: /2

4. Forgetful Fiona has lost the measurements for the length and width of a shape that she measured. Use the following clues to work out the length and width:
   - The shape was a rectangle.
   - The length was 3 times the width.
   - The perimeter was 48 m.

**Top tip:** There are different ways to solve this puzzle. You could use the letter '*x*' to represent the missing width and write a number sentence to find the missing value. Alternatively, you could use the strategy of trial and improvement.

Answer: length = width = Marks: /2



Today's Marks: /8

## Day Four Try these.

1. The Simpsons' skipping ropes are all jumbled up! If Maggie's skipping rope measures 0.8 m, can you work out the length of the other skipping ropes?

   - Homer's skipping rope is double the length of Maggie's.
   - Maggie's skipping rope is $\frac{2}{3}$ the length of Bart's.
   - Homer's skipping rope is $\frac{3}{5}$ m longer than Lisa's.
   - Marge's skipping rope is 0.4 m longer than Lisa's.

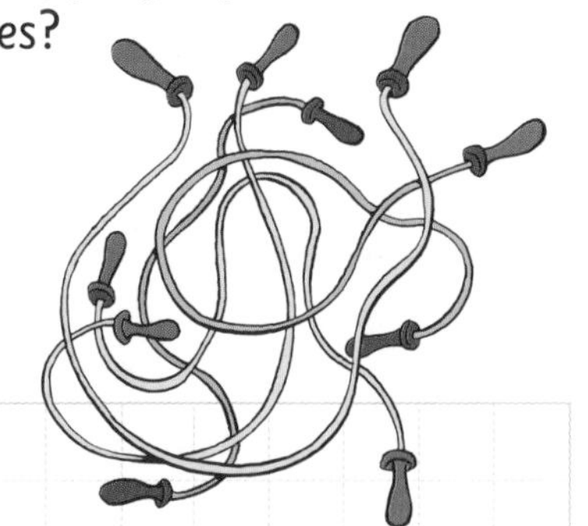

**Answers:** Homer's ______ Bart's ______ Lisa's ______ Marge's ______ **Marks:** ___ /4

2. Rewrite the answers from question 1 in cm.

**Answers:** Homer's ______ Bart's ______ Lisa's ______ Marge's ______ **Marks:** ___ /4

3. Springfield Primary School needs a new fence around its yard. Before the principal can order one, she needs to find out the perimeter. The yard has five sides. The first measures 12.75 m, the second is 3.15 m longer than the first and each subsequent side is 3.15 m longer than the last. Can you work out the perimeter of the yard?

**Answer:** ______ **Marks:** ___ /2

**Today's Marks:** ___ /10

## Super Sleuth investigates

A lap of the track at the Bird's Nest Stadium in Beijing is 0.4 km long. If Usain Bolt can run 100 m in 9.79 seconds, how long would it take him to run a full lap if he maintains this speed throughout?

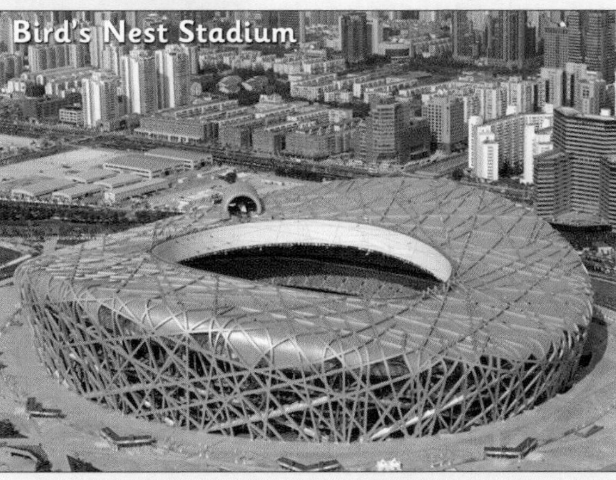
Bird's Nest Stadium

Usain Bolt

Use a trundle wheel to measure 100 m in your school hall or yard. Time how long it takes you to run 100 m. Compare your performance with that of Usain Bolt!

**Total Marks:** ___ /32 | **I was able to complete the perimeter tasks.** Yes ☐ No ☐

**I used these strategies in this unit:** ______

# 16 Weight

**We are learning to:** Rename measurements of weight using fractions and decimals. ☐
Work backwards to solve puzzles. ☐

## Day One

**Study the steps used to solve the problem in the example below.**

A rugby player lifted 170 kg during weight training on Friday, half this weight on Saturday and 195 kg on Sunday. What was the average weight that he lifted over the three days?

**Circle the numbers and keywords:** 170 kg, half, 195 kg, average

**Link with operation needed (+, –, × or ÷):** Add (+). Divide (÷).

**Use a strategy:** Simplify – break it into steps.

**Estimate and calculate:**

| My estimate: around 160 kg | 170 kg<br>85 kg<br>+ 195 kg<br>450 kg | 450 kg ÷ 3 = 150 kg | **Answer:** 150 kg |
|---|---|---|---|

**Summarise and check how you got your answer:**
I worked out the weights lifted, then added the three weights and divided by 3 to find the average.

### Try these.

The following table shows the combined weight of six men's rugby teams:

| Ireland | England | Wales | France | Scotland | Italy |
|---|---|---|---|---|---|
| 1,533 kg | 1,532 kg | 1,568 kg | 1,513 kg | 1,512 kg | 1,474 kg |

1. **(a)** What is the total weight of the teams?
**(b)** What is the average weight of the teams?

Answers: (a) ____ (b) ____ Marks: ____ /4

2. If the Irish women's rugby team weighs $\frac{2}{3}$ of the weight of the Irish men's team, how much does the women's team weigh?

Answer: ____ Marks: ____ /2

3. There are 15 players on the Irish men's team. What is the average weight of each player?

Answer: ____ Marks: ____ /2



Today's Marks: ____ /8

# Day Two Try these.

1. You are going to Spain for 5 nights and you are allowed to carry luggage weighing up to 10 kg. In your copy, work out what you will bring. You will need a different outfit for every day and remember that your suitcase weighs 2.75 kg when it is empty.

| Pair of flip-flops 250 g | Shorts 220 g | Sunglasses 525 g | Jewellery 750 g | Towel 800 g | Swimwear 190 g |
|---|---|---|---|---|---|
| Phrase book 675 g | iPod 150 g | Handbag 750 g | Travel adapter 325 g | Pyjamas 350 g | Toothpaste 100 g |
| Pair of socks 190 g | Sun hat 120 g | Guide book 495 g | First-aid kit 645 g | Phone 140 g | Cardigan 485 g |
| Pair of runners 705 g | T-shirt 175 g | Hairbrush 330 g | Toothbrush 225 g | Jeans 550 g | Passport 45 g |

**Marks:** /2

2. **(a)** How much does your packed suitcase weigh? **(b)** How much less is this than the 10 kg limit?

**Answers: (a)** **(b)** **Marks:** /4

3. Jane thinks that if you add up all of the items in the green boxes above, they will be heavier than all of the items in the yellow and blue boxes. Tom disagrees. Who is right? Make a prediction before you work it out.

**Answer:** **Marks:** /2

4. Jane and Tom have each packed 5 items in a suitcase. Their suitcases don't have any items in common, but the total weight of the five items they have each chosen is 1,000 g. Can you suggest what five items **(a)** Jane and **(b)** Tom may have chosen?

**Answers: (a)** **(b)** **Marks:** /2

**Today's Marks:** /10

## Day Three Try these.

Cian has a new job at a local animal shelter for the summer. He is responsible for ordering food for his furry friends. Can you help him to fill in his order sheet for this week?

**Top tip:** You will need to use the strategy of working backwards to find some of the missing values.

| Animal | Breakfast | Lunch | Supper | Daily Total | Weekly Total (7 days) | Unit Price | Total Cost |
|---|---|---|---|---|---|---|---|
| 1 Meerkat | 25 g | 25 g | ___ g | | 525 g or 0.525 kg | €28 per 500 g | |
| 2 Cat | 125 g | 125 g | 125 g | | | €6.40 per 1 kg | |
| 3 Pony | 700 g | ___ g | 850 g | | 17,500 g or 17.5 kg | €2.60 per 500 g | |
| 4 Alpaca | 1,600 g | 800 g | 1,350 g | | | €2 per 1 kg | |



Today's Marks: /24

## Day Four Try these.

1 A boat can carry a maximum weight of 65 kg. Mr Kelly weighs 62 kg, Mrs Kelly weighs 56 kg and their two children weigh 31 kg and 27 kg respectively. What is the fewest number of boat trips needed to carry this family across the river?

**Top tip:** Act it out or draw diagrams showing the family's movements.

Answer: ______ Marks: ___ /2

2 Why is the Mississippi River so unusual? Crack the code to find out!

| A | B | C | D | E | F | G |
|---|---|---|---|---|---|---|
| 500 g | 1 kg 700 g | Weighing scales | 0.2 kg | $\frac{3}{8}$ kg | 750 g | 1 kg |
| **H** | **I** | **J** | **K** | **L** | **M** | **N** |
| $\frac{2}{25}$ kg | 50% | $\frac{7}{12}$ kg | 0.025 kg | $1\frac{3}{4}$ kg | 55 g | 450 g |
| **O** | **P** | **Q** | **R** | **S** | **T** | |
| 252 g | $\frac{17}{20}$ kg | 9 kg 5 g | $1\frac{1}{4}$ kg | 70 kg | 5,000 g | |
| **U** | **V** | **W** | **X** | **Y** | **Z** | |
| 1 kg 50 g | 800 g | 1 kg | 15% | gram | $\frac{13}{16}$ kg | |

| 500 g as a % of 1 kg | 5 kg | 80 g | $\frac{1}{2}$ kg | 8.75 kg × 8 = |
|---|---|---|---|---|
| | | | | |
| $\frac{3}{4}$ kg | 45 g as a % of 90 g | $\frac{4}{5}$ kg | 1,055 g – 680 g = | 0.375 kg |
| | | | | |
| Unit of measurement | 1 kg – $\frac{5}{8}$ kg = | Weight of a man | $1\frac{7}{10}$ kg | 725 g + 325 g = |
| | | | | |
| 250 g × 20 = | Instrument for weighing food | $\frac{3}{5}$ kg – $\frac{1}{10}$ kg = | $\frac{2}{5}$ kg + 0.05 kg = | 1.25 kg × 4 = |
| | | | | |
| 61.25 kg + 8.75 kg = | 375 g | 175 g + 0.2 kg = | | |
| | | | | |

Marks: ___ /46

Today's Marks: ___ /48

Total Marks: ___ /90 My favourite activity in this unit was ______

My least favourite activity in this unit was ______

# 17 Area and Perimeter

**We are learning to:** Calculate the area of 2-D and 3-D shapes. ☐ Calculate the area of a room from a scale plan. ☐ Investigate the relationship between area and perimeter. ☐

## Day One

**Study the steps used to solve the problem in the example below.**

Draw a quadrilateral with a perimeter of 30 cm and an area of 36 cm$^2$.

CLUES

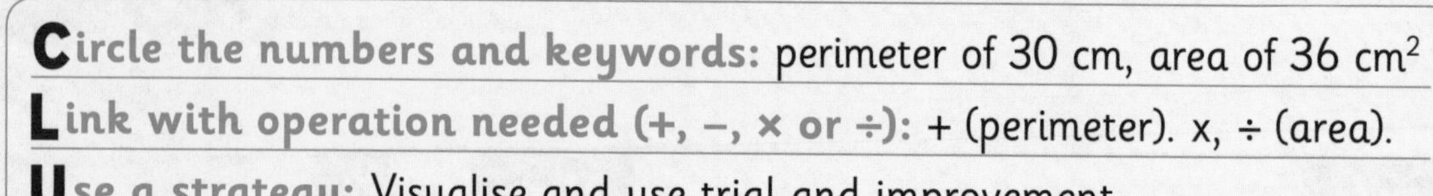

**Circle the numbers and keywords:** perimeter of 30 cm, area of 36 cm$^2$

**Link with operation needed (+, –, × or ÷):** + (perimeter). x, ÷ (area).

**Use a strategy:** Visualise and use trial and improvement.

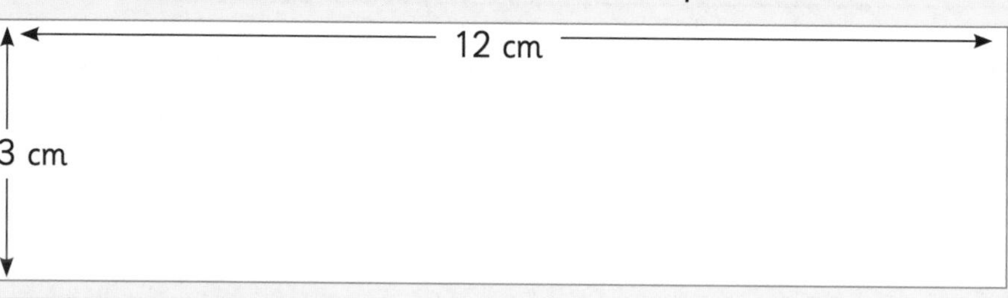


**Estimate and calculate:**

Perimeter = 12 cm + 12 cm + 3 cm + 3 cm = 30 cm

Area = 12 cm x 3 cm = 36 cm$^2$

**Summarise and check how you got your answer:**

I drew all of the quadrilaterals with an area of 36 cm$^2$ and found just one with a perimeter of 30 cm.

**Top tip:**
To solve this puzzle, draw all quadrilaterals with an area of 36 m$^2$ in order to find one that has a perimeter of 30 cm.

### Try these.

CLUES

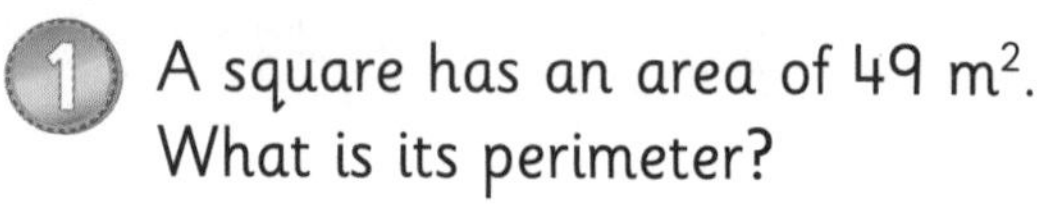

1. A square has an area of 49 m$^2$. What is its perimeter?

**Answer:** **Marks:** /2

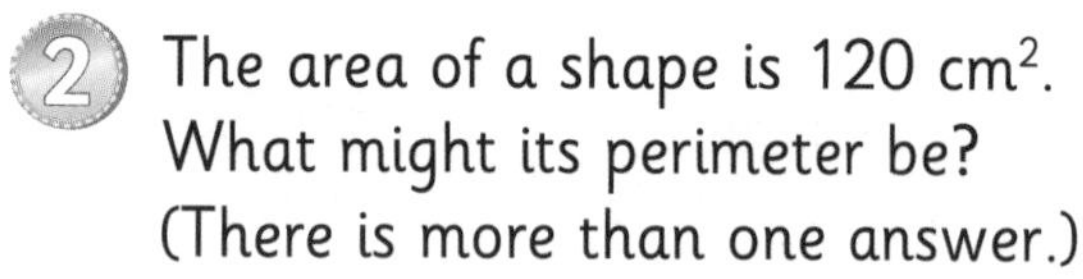

2. The area of a shape is 120 cm$^2$. What might its perimeter be? (There is more than one answer.)

**Answer:** **Marks:** /2

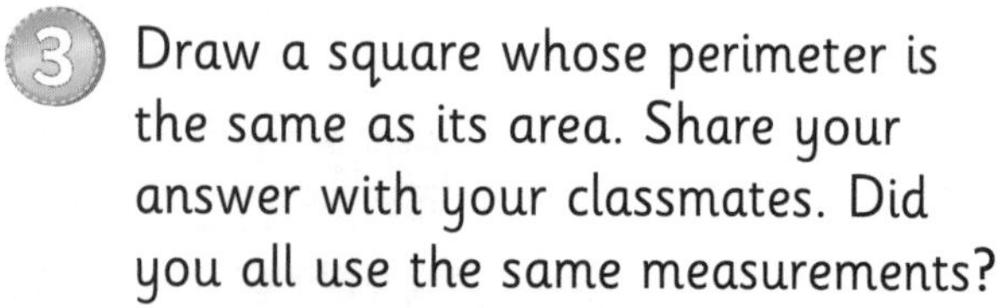

3. Draw a square whose perimeter is the same as its area. Share your answer with your classmates. Did you all use the same measurements?

**Marks:** /2

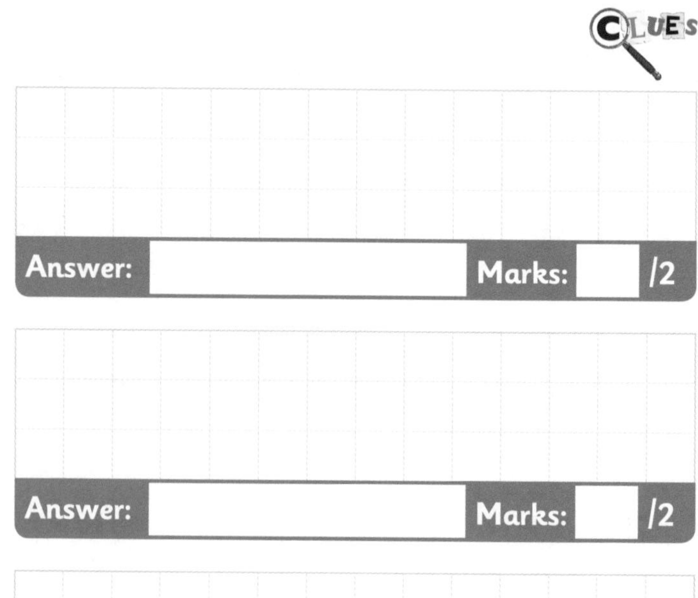



**Strand:** Measures **Strand Units:** Area; Length

**Today's Marks:** /6

## Day Two Try these.

CLUEs

ABCDEFGHIJKLM
NOPQRSTUVWXYZ

1. Draw your name on the 1 cm squares below in the same style as the image above.

Marks: /2

2. What is the area that you have used for your name? (Hint: Count the squares to find out the area of your name!)

Answer: $cm^2$ Marks: /2

3. What is the average area used for the names of the pupils in your group?

Answer: $cm^2$ Marks: /2

4. An Irish television company has decided to create its own version of *The Cube*. Can you figure out what the surface area of the cube will be in $m^2$ if each side measures 4.5 cm on the plan and the scale is 1 $cm^2$ = 1 $m^2$?

Answer: $m^2$ Marks: /2

Today's Marks: /8

## Day Three Try these.

CLUES

1. Find the area of this shape. Divide the shape into two rectangles to make it easier.

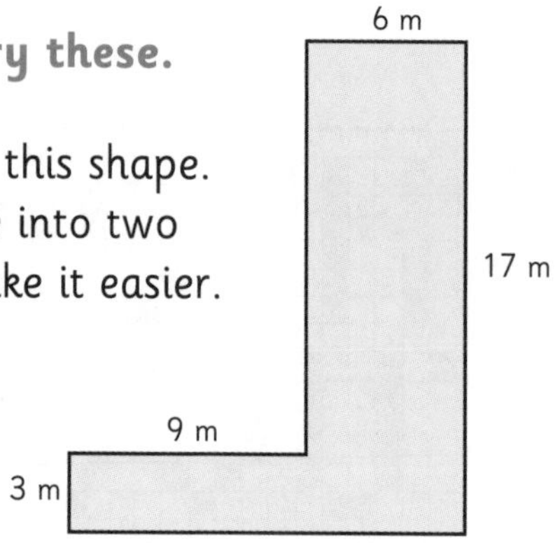

6 m
17 m
9 m
3 m

Answer: m² Marks: /2

2. Find the area of this shape.

7.5 m
2.5 m
10 m
4.5 m

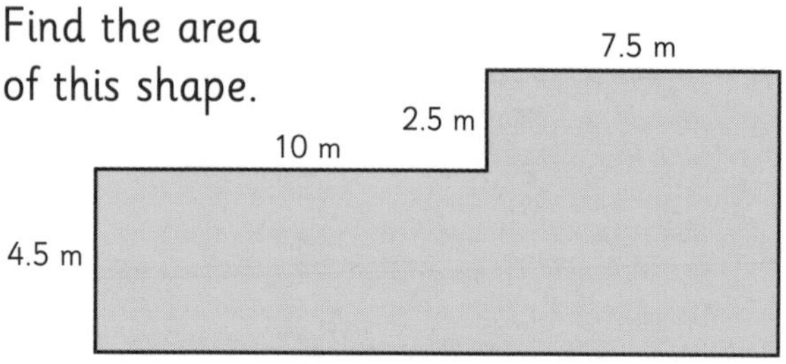

Answer: m² Marks: /2

3. Liam's family will rent a room in a hotel for his birthday party and they want to choose the cheapest room. The room with the smallest area is more expensive, because it has beautiful views of a lake. Find the area of each room below if the scale is 1 $cm^2$ = 1 $m^2$. Which room should they choose? Tick your answer.

(a) The Party Suite

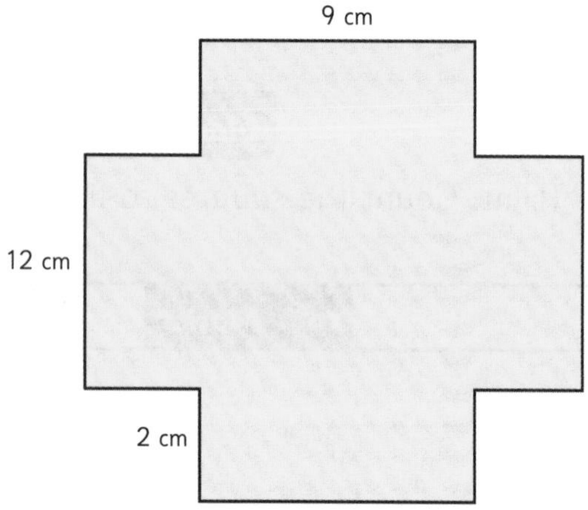

9 cm
12 cm
2 cm

(b) The Disco Destination

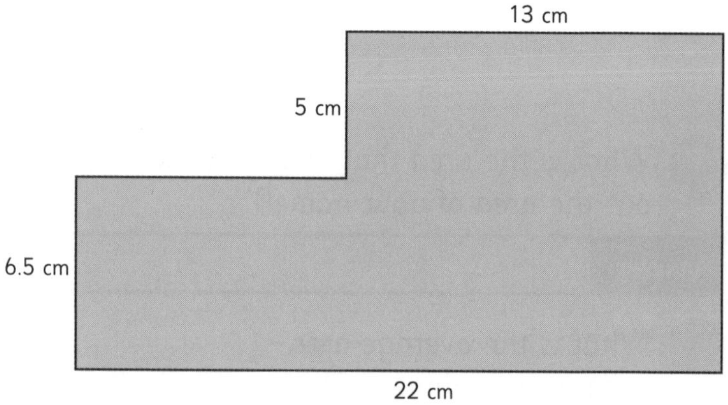

13 cm
5 cm
6.5 cm
22 cm

**Top tip:** This room has an unusual shape because four square corner sections were removed to build bathrooms.

Answers: (a) m² (b) m² Marks: /4



Today's Marks: /8

## Day Four Try these.

CLUES

1. Draw a quadrilateral with a perimeter of 22 cm and an area of 24 $cm^2$.

Marks: /2

2. The perimeter of a shape is 108 cm. Its length is 5 times its width. What is its area?

Answer: $cm^2$ Marks: /2

3. This shape is made of squares. The area of the entire shape is 160 $cm^2$. What is the perimeter of the shape?

Answer: cm Marks: /2

Today's Marks: /6

## Super Sleuth investigates

Find the following items and measure their surface area: **1.** a Rubik's Cube, **2.** a die, **3.** a mathematical set, **4.** a lunch box.

## Super Sleuth investigates

1. As a class, draw squares with an area of 100 $cm^2$ on sheets of paper. Cut them out and create a small image of a good memory from your time in primary school.
2. Use a metre stick to create a poster measuring 1 $m^2$. Compare the two. Predict how many of the smaller pieces would fit onto the poster.
3. Place enough of the good memory squares together until you have a larger square measuring 1 $m^2$. Was your prediction correct?
4. Place the individual pieces together to create a beautiful class collage of your happiest moments in primary school.

Total Marks: /28 | The maths language that I used in this unit includes the following words:

I would like to find out what means.

# 18 Revision 3

## Thrillzone Theme Park

### Day One Try these.

1. Thrillzone used to be square-shaped, but a new car park was built, using up one-quarter of its area. **(a)** If the perimeter was 1,648 m before the car park was built, estimate and then work out the new perimeter. **(b)** What is the new area of Thrillzone, not including the car park?

Car park

**Answers: (a)** ______ **(b)** ______ m² **Marks:** ___ /4

2. There are different lengths for each of the four Thrillzone ziplines – blue, red, yellow and green. Place the colours in order from the shortest to the longest using the following clues:
   - The red zip line is neither the longest nor the shortest zip line.
   - The blue zip line is shorter than the red zip line.
   - The green zip line is longer than the red zip line.
   - The blue zip line is not the shortest zip line.

**Answer:** ______ **Marks:** ___ /2

3. Lena noticed that the Crazy Golf Zone was in the shape of a regular pentagon and its perimeter was 17.5 cm on the map. **(a)** Draw this shape in the box provided. **(b)** If the scale used on the map was 1 cm = 2.5 m, what was the real perimeter of the Crazy Golf Zone?

**Answer: (b)** ______ **Marks:** ___ /2



**Strand:** Shape and Space **Strand Unit:** 2-D Shapes
**Strand:** Measures **Strand Units:** Length; Weight; Area

**Today's Marks:** ___ /8

# Day Two Try these.

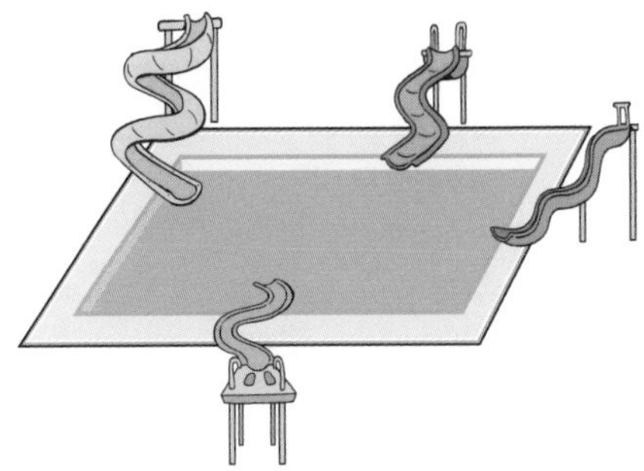

1. Four water slides lead into a rectangular swimming pool with an area of 56 $m^2$. What might the perimeter of the pool be? (There are more than three possible answers.)

**Answer:** m **Marks:** /2

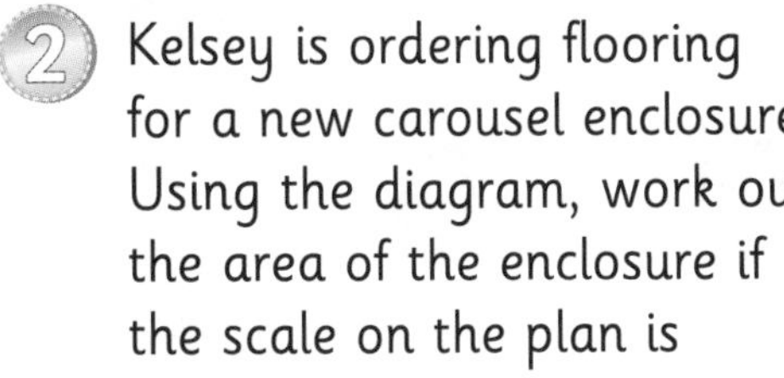

2. Kelsey is ordering flooring for a new carousel enclosure. Using the diagram, work out the area of the enclosure if the scale on the plan is 1 cm = 1 m.

12.5 cm
3.5 cm
8.5 cm
29 cm

**Answer:** $m^2$ **Marks:** /2

3. Thrillzone is building a House of Horrors as shown. Work out the surface area of the House of Horrors in $m^2$ if the scale is 1 cm = 1 m.

**Answer:** $m^2$ **Marks:** /2

## Super Sleuth investigates

Set up circuits in your school. Each group member completes every task at the circuits. Add together the measurements recorded at each circuit. The winning team will have the greatest total length recorded at the end of the competition. Choose from the following circuits: standing jump, javelin, bean bag hop, paper aeroplane. Check out the 5th and 6th Class maths trails for more information.

**Today's Marks:** /6

## Day Three

Try these.

CLUES

1. The maximum weight allowed in each compartment on the Ferris wheel is 220.5 kg. If there are 12 compartments, what is the total maximum weight allowed?

Answer: Marks: /2

2. Look at the table. **(a)** What is the combined weight of this family? **(b)** Would they be allowed to ride in a single compartment on the Ferris wheel above?

| The Carty Family | | | | |
|---|---|---|---|---|
| Mum | Grandad | Evelyn | Dora | Leon |
| 60.75 kg | 61.5 kg | 41.8 kg | 33.9 kg | 34.85 kg |

Answers: (a) (b) Marks: /4

3. Evelyn, Dora and Leon Carty bought an average of 375 g of pick 'n' mix sweets. If Evelyn's sweets weighed 515 g and Dora's weighed 295 g, how much did Leon's weigh?

Answer: Marks: /2

4. The Pirate Boat ride can carry a maximum weight of 110.5 kg and must have a minimum weight of 95.5 kg. What combinations of Carty family members could take the boat together?

Answer: Marks: /2



Today's Marks: /10

## Day Four Try these.

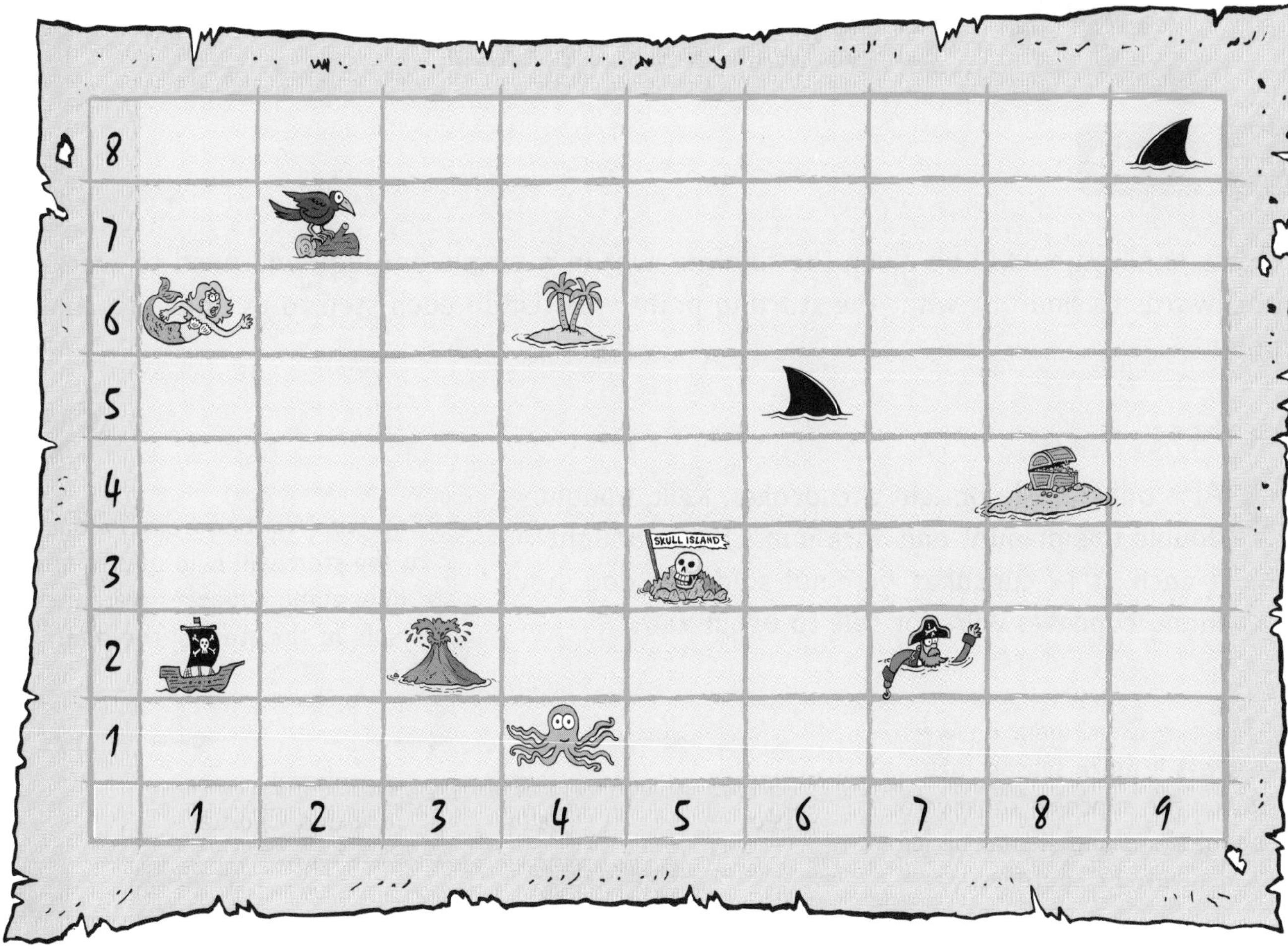

| 8 | | | | | | | | | |
|---|---|---|---|---|---|---|---|---|---|
| 7 | | | | | | | | | |
| 6 | | | | | | | | | |
| 5 | | | | | | | | | |
| 4 | | | | | | | | | |
| 3 | | | | | SKULL ISLAND | | | | |
| 2 | | | | | | | | | |
| 1 | | | | | | | | | |
| | 1 | 2 | 3 | 4 | 5 | 6 | 7 | 8 | 9 |

1. Look at the map. Write the co-ordinates where you would find the following:
   **(a)** a pirate ship ______ **(b)** Skull Island ______
   **(c)** a treasure chest ______
   **Marks: /3**

2. Draw the following items in the co-ordinates written next to them:
   **(a)** an anchor (8, 7) **(b)** a compass (9, 1) **(c)** a shark (3, 4)
   **Marks: /3**

3. Draw a route between the pirate ship and the treasure chest on the map. You must avoid the sharks and Skull Island. Write the co-ordinates of the boxes that you travelled through and compare your route with that of a partner.

**Answer:** ______ **Marks: /2**

**Today's Marks: /8**

### Super Sleuth challenge

In your copy, draw a grid with 8 rows and 8 columns. Choose one of the following 2-D shapes to draw in your grid: pentagon, rhombus, trapezium; hexagon. Write the co-ordinates of your shape.

### Puzzle power

In groups, play 'Who Am I?'. One pupil in each group wears a post-it note with the name of a mystery 2-D shape on it. They must ask 10 questions using specific maths language to help them work out the shape. The answers must be 'yes' or 'no'.

**Total Marks: /32**

# 19 Strategy: Working Backwards

## Day One

Occasionally, you will be given the final answer in a puzzle and you will need to work backwards to find out what the starting point was. Undo each step to get back to that point.

**Try these.**

1. At a bakery, Isla bought 3 cupcakes, Kelly bought double this amount and Jack and Charlie bought 1 each. If 17 cupcakes were not sold that day, how many cupcakes were for sale to begin with?

**Top tip:** Working from 17 back to the start will help you to find how many cupcakes were for sale at the start of the day.

**Top tip:** Check your answer. Does it make sense? Take away the cupcakes that were bought and you should be left with 17 cupcakes.

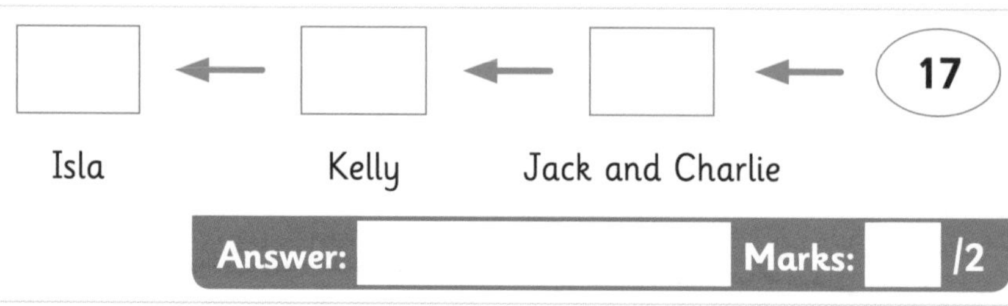


**Answer:** ______ **Marks:** ___ /2

2. In a gift shop, Paul bought a pencil for €0.85, a soft toy for €4.95 and a diary for €6.95. He received €2.25 in change from the cashier. How much money did he give the cashier in the first place?

**Answer:** ______ **Marks:** ___ /2

3. Patrick decided to go on a tour of Pine Valley Farm on the mini train. The train pulled up at a stop and 10 people, including Patrick, got on. At the next stop, 5 people got off and twice as many people got on than at the previous stop. At the next stop, 15 people got off and there were 17 people left on the train. How many people had been on the train to begin with (before Patrick got on)?

**Answer:** ______ **Marks:** ___ /2

**Today's Marks:** ___ /6

## Day Two Try these.

CLUES

1. A lamb is fifteen times the weight of a rabbit. A rabbit is $\frac{1}{30}$ the weight of a deer. If a deer weighs 90 kg, how much does a lamb weigh?

Answer: Marks: /2

2. Pine Valley Farm has 6 more calves than dogs. It has three fewer pigs than calves. 25 of the animals are baby animals (calves and lambs). There are 10 lambs. How many dogs and pigs does the farm have altogether?

**Top tip:** Make a table to help you organise the information.

Answer: Marks: /2

3. Daddy Giraffe's neck is double the length of Baby Giraffe's neck. Mammy Giraffe's neck is 79 cm longer than Baby Giraffe's neck. Granny Giraffe's neck is 8 cm shorter than Mammy Giraffe's neck and measures 1.66 m long. How long is Daddy Giraffe's neck?

Answer: Marks: /2

4. A senior citizen's ticket for Pine Valley Farm is twice the price of a child's. An adult's ticket is 4 times the price of a child's. If an adult's ticket costs €15, how much would 6 senior citizens pay?

Answer: Marks: /2

Today's Marks: /8

## Day Three Try these.

CLUES

1. Tweety and his family live in a cage shaped like a cube. If the volume of the cube is 64 $m^3$, what is the length of one of the sides of the cage?

**Top tip:** length × width × height = volume

**Answer:** **Marks:** /2

2. Using the answer to question 1 (the length of one side), work out the surface area of Tweety's cage.

**Answer:** **Marks:** /2

3. Pine Valley Farm held a raffle last March. The three prizes added up to €400. The 1st prize was 2.5 times bigger than the 3rd prize. The 2nd prize was $\frac{3}{5}$ of the 1st prize. If the third prize was €80, what was the value of **(a)** the 1st prize and **(b)** the 2nd prize?

**Answers: (a)** **(b)** **Marks:** /4

4. Danielle spent 4 minutes in the queue to buy tickets for Pine Valley Farm, 14 minutes on the mini train, 12 minutes in the gift shop and 1 hour and 5 minutes walking around the farm. If Danielle left the farm at 5:20 pm, at what time did she arrive?

**Answer:** **Marks:** /2



**Today's Marks:** /10

## Day Four Try these.

CLUES

1. Yuri thought of a number. He multiplied it by 7, then added 12 and ended up with 110. What number did he start with?

**Top tip:** Begin at 110 and undo each step to find the number that Yuri started with.

**Answer:** **Marks:** /2

2. is a number. If you multiply by 9, you get . If you add 13 to , you will get $7^2$. What is the value of ?

**Answer:** **Marks:** /2

3. is a number. I found one-quarter of it and got . I divided by 3 and got . When I took 34 from , I was left with $2^3$. What is the value of ?

**Answer:** **Marks:** /2

**Today's Marks:** /6

## Super Sleuth challenge

Create your own puzzle that requires the strategy of working backwards to solve it. Share it with a partner.

## Puzzle power

Nim is a strategy game that has been played by maths students all over the world. It is around 1,000 years old! You can use unifix cubes to play this game in pairs.

1. Place 16 cubes on your desk between you and your partner.
2. Each player takes turns picking up 1, 2, 3 or 4 cubes at a time.
3. The player who is left with the last cube loses.

Play this game a few times with your partner. Devise a strategy that will ensure you win every time. Try out your plan a few times. Did it work?

**Total Marks:** /30 | **I can work backwards to solve a maths puzzle.** Yes No

**I will use this strategy in future when**

Week 20

# 20 Time

**We are learning to:** Explore international time zones. ☐
Explore the relationship between time, distance and average speed. ☐

## Day One Try these.

1. Recently, people began to notice that their town clock was slowing down. It was reset each night at 1 am, but it lost 2.5 minutes every hour. What time did it show when the real time was 11 am? Use the table below to help you.

| **Real time:** | 1 am | 2 am | 3 am | | | |
|---|---|---|---|---|---|---|
| **Town clock:** | 1 am | 1:57:30 am | | | | |

| **Real time:** | | | | | |
|---|---|---|---|---|---|
| **Town clock:** | | | | | |

**Answer:** ______ **Marks:** /2

2. The woman who fixed the clock sent an unusual bill for her work. It didn't include the cost of her work, but instead contained this puzzle: "The cost of my work is three times the number of minutes that the clock lost between 1 am and 11 am, plus VAT at 15%." Can you work out how much money she was owed?

**Answer:** ______ **Marks:** /2

3. At what time should Marco put **(a)** the turkey and **(b)** the goose into the oven to ensure that each is fully cooked by 5:30 pm? The turkey weighs 8 kg and the goose weighs 4.5 kg.

**Cooking Times**

**Turkey:** 20 mins per 1 kg plus an extra 90 mins

**Goose:** 15 mins per 500 g plus an extra 30 mins

**Answers: (a)** ______ **(b)** ______ **Marks:** /2



**Today's Marks:** /6

# Day Two Try these.

1. Martha is flying from Shannon to Boston at 2:40 pm to visit her brother John. The flight will take 7 hours 15 minutes and then it will take Martha 35 minutes to collect her suitcases from the baggage hall. At what time should John turn up at the arrivals area of the airport to meet Martha if Shannon is 4 hours ahead of Boston?

**Answer:** **Marks:** /2

2. Miss O'Brien's class is going to participate in a Fairtrade project with three schools in other countries. The pupils will need to make Skype calls in order to work together. The school day in each participating school is from 9 am until 2:40 pm local time. Use the information in the table to decide which three schools Miss O'Brien's class should work with. Explain your decision.

| School | Time Difference |
|---|---|
| (a) San Francisco Middle School | –7 hours |
| (b) St Petersburg Primary School | +3 hours |
| (c) Sydney Senior School | +10 hours |
| (d) Rome Regional School | +1 hours |
| (e) Rio de Janeiro Primary School | –4 hours |

**Answer:**

**Marks:** /2

3. Four pupils were chosen from Miss O'Brien's class to visit San Francisco Middle School. They were due to depart from Dublin Airport at 9:10 am, but their flight was delayed by 1 hour and 40 minutes. If the duration of the flight was 11 hours and 5 minutes, what was the local time in San Francisco when their flight landed?

**Answer:** **Marks:** /2

**Today's Marks:** /6

## Day Three

**Try these.**

**1** During World War II, a group of children being evacuated from London boarded the 1:45 pm train to Cornwall. The train was delayed by 27 minutes. The journey then took 2 hours and 16 minutes. At what time did the children reach their destination?

**Answer:** | **Marks:** /2

**2** Use the information in the triangle to fill in the missing information about military vehicles used during World War II.

| Transport | Country | Time | Distance | Speed |
|---|---|---|---|---|
| Dornier Do | Germany | 2 hours | 1,526 km | |
| Spitfire | Britain | 4.25 hours | | 795 km/h |
| U-Boat | Germany | | 222.75 km | 33 km/h |
| BT-8 Tank | Soviet Union | 3.5 hours | 301 km | |

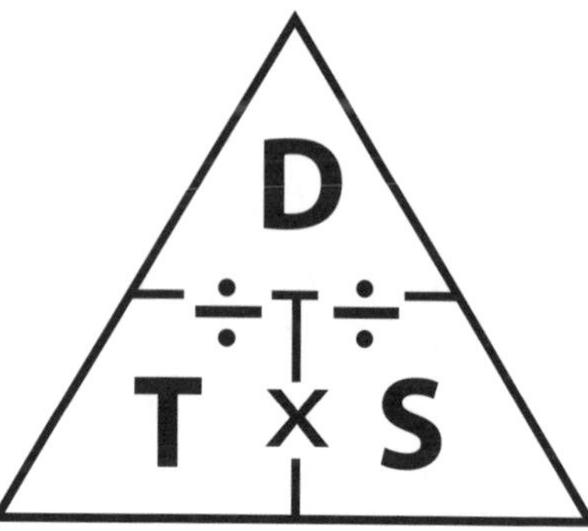


**Answer:** | **Marks:** /8

**3** At Bletchley Park, Britain's codebreakers worked to decode the messages sent between German military forces. Can you break the following pigpen code to work out at what time the Germans were planning an air raid over London?
Fill in the answer on the clock.

| A | B | C |
|---|---|---|
| D | E | F |
| G | H | I |

| J | K | L |
|---|---|---|
| M | N | O |
| P | Q | R |

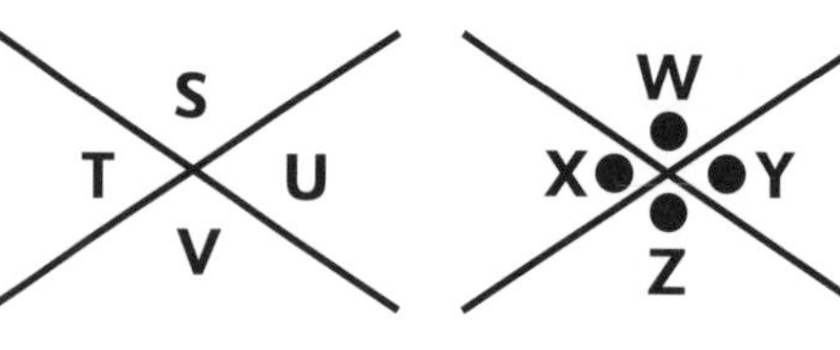


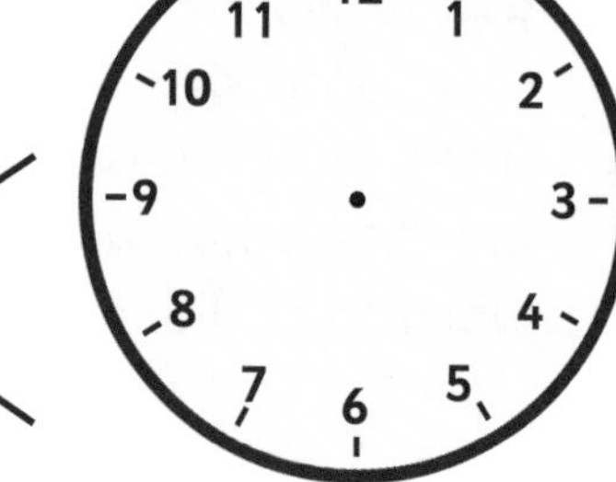


**Message:**

**Answer:** | **Marks:** /4



**Today's Marks:** /14

# Day Four Try these.

You will start secondary school very soon and you will use a timetable like the following to organise the books that you need for your classes:

| Time | Monday | Tuesday | Wednesday | Thursday | Friday |
|---|---|---|---|---|---|
| 9 am | Assembly | Assembly | Assembly | Assembly | Assembly |
| 9:10 am | English | Irish | Maths | Geography | English |
| 9:50 am | Maths | English | CSPE | Irish | Maths |
| 10:30 am | Irish | Maths | History | English | Irish |
| **11:10 am** | **B** | **R** | **E** | **A** | **K** |
| 11:30 am | French OR Spanish | Home Economics OR Art | English | Maths | Technology |
| 12:10 pm | Geography | Home Economics OR Art | Irish | Business Studies | Science |
| **12:50 pm** | **L** | **U** | **N** | **C** | **H** |
| 1:40 pm | History | Religion | | Maths | Religion |
| 2:20 pm | Business Studies | Technical Graphics OR Metalwork | | Science | French OR Spanish |
| 3:00 pm | Physical Education | Technical Graphics OR Metalwork | | Music | Physical Education |

1. Which day would you most look forward to? Explain.

**Answer:** **Marks:** /2

2. Which day would you not look forward to? Explain.

**Answer:** **Marks:** /2

3. Why do you think there is a gap in the timetable on Wednesday?

**Answer:** **Marks:** /2

4. On Wednesday, I was 1,800 seconds late for school. At 9:45 am, I left school for an appointment. I returned to school at 11 am. How long did I spend in class on Wednesday?

**Answer:** **Marks:** /2

**Today's Marks:** /8

**Total Marks:** /34 **I feel confident about problem-solving when**

**My teacher can help me by**

# 21 Number Theory

**We are learning to:** Identify simple prime and composite numbers. ☐ Identify and explore square and cubed numbers. ☐ Identify common factors and multiples. ☐

## Day One Try these.

1. Draw a diagram that represents $5^2$ and fill in the missing values based on your diagram.

   ___ × ___ = ___$^2$ = ___

Marks: /2

2. Find a number under 100 which is both a square and a cubed number.

Answer: Marks: /2

3. Which numbers between 1 and 30 have three factors?

Answer: Marks: /2

4. Abundant numbers occur when the sum of the factors of a number, not including itself, are greater than the number itself. For example, 12 is an abundant number, because its factors (not including itself), 1, 2, 3, 4 and 6, add up to 16. Complete your own investigation. You have two minutes to find as many abundant numbers under 100 as possible.

Answer: Marks: /2

## Super Sleuth challenge

Decide which labels from the list below you think this Venn diagram should include. Then, create your own Venn diagram puzzle using these labels.

| Prime Numbers | Composite Numbers |
|---|---|
| Odd Numbers | Even Numbers |
| Multiples of 3 | Square numbers |
| Factors of 64 | Between 7 and 28 |

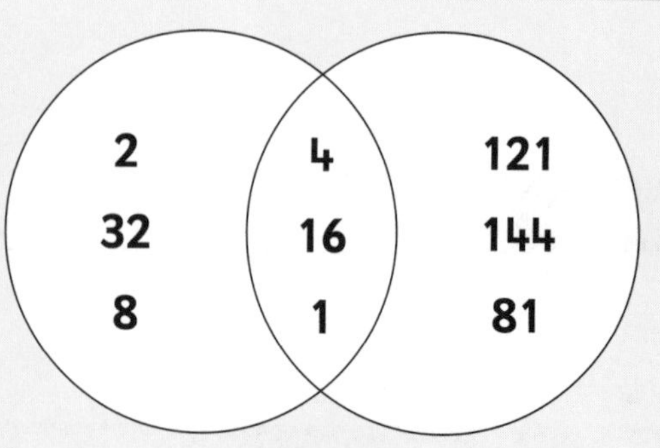




Today's Marks: /8

# 21 Number Theory

**We are learning to:** Identify simple prime and composite numbers. ☐ Identify and explore square and cubed numbers. ☐ Identify common factors and multiples. ☐

## Day One Try these.

Draw a diagram that represents $5^2$ and fill in the missing values based on your diagram

$$\_\_ \times \_\_ = \_\_^2 = \_\_$$

Marks: /2

Find a number under 100 which is both a square and a cubed number.

Answer:

Which numbers between 1 and 30 have three factors?

Answer:

Marks: /2

Abundant numbers occur when the sum of the factors of a number, not including itself, are greater than the number itself. For example, 12 is an abundant number, because its factors (not including itself), 1, 2, 3, 4 and 6, add up to 16. Complete your own investigation. You have two minutes to find as many abundant numbers under 100 as possible.

Answer:

Marks: /2

## Super Sleuth challenge

Decide which labels from the list below you think this Venn diagram should include. Then, create your own Venn diagram puzzle using these labels.

| Prime Numbers | Composite Numbers |
|---|---|
| Odd Numbers | Even Numbers |
| Multiples of 3 | Square numbers |
| Factors of 64 | Between 7 and 28 |

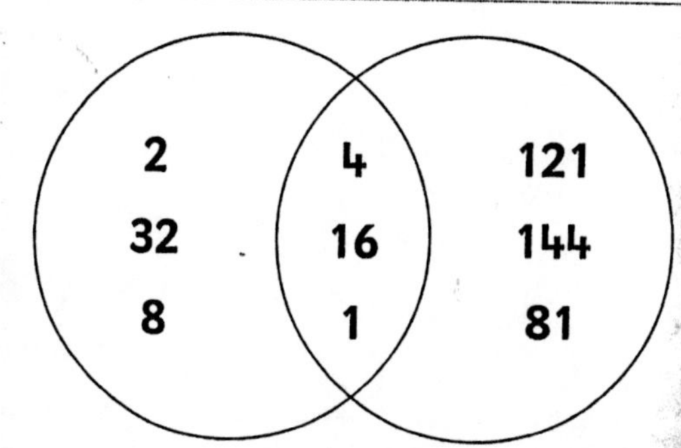




Today's Marks: /8

# 21 Number Theory

**We are learning to:** Identify simple prime and composite numbers. ▢ Identify and explore square and cubed numbers. ▢ Identify common factors and multiples. ▢

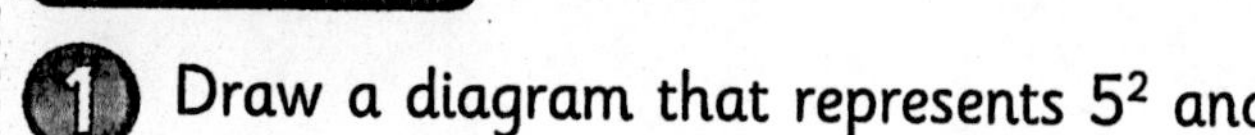

## Day One Try these.

1. Draw a diagram that represents $5^2$ and fill in the missing values based on your diagram

× = ² =

Marks: /2

2. Find a number under 100 which is both a square and a cubed number.

Answer:

Marks: /2

3. Which numbers between 1 and 30 have three factors?

Answer:

Marks: /2

4. Abundant numbers occur when the sum of the factors of a number, not including itself, are greater than the number itself. For example, 12 is an abundant number, because its factors (not including itself), 1, 2, 3, 4 and 6, add up to 16. Complete your own investigation. You have two minutes to find as many abundant numbers under 100 as possible.

Answer:

Marks: /2

## Super Sleuth challenge

Decide which labels from the list below you think this Venn diagram should include. Then, create your own Venn diagram puzzle using these labels.

| Prime Numbers | Composite Numbers |
|---|---|
| Odd Numbers | Even Numbers |
| Multiples of 3 | Square numbers |
| Factors of 64 | Between 7 and 28 |

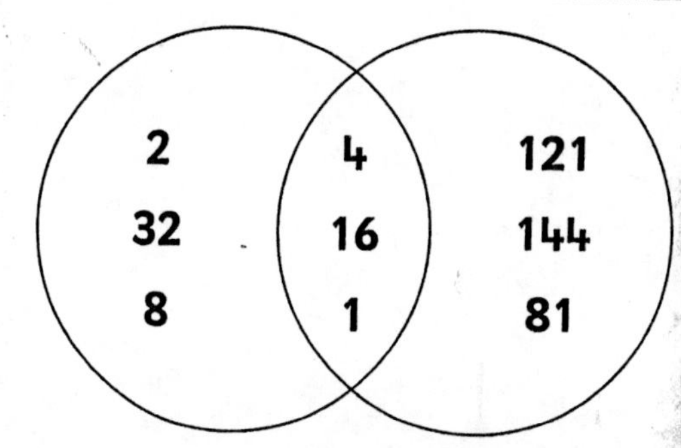




**Strand:** Number **Strand Unit:** Number Theory

Today's Marks: /8

# 21 Number Theory

**We are learning to:** Identify simple prime and composite numbers. ▢ Identify and explore square and cubed numbers. ▢ Identify common factors and multiples. ▢

## Day One Try these.

1. Draw a diagram that represents $5^2$ and fill in the missing values based on your diagran

   × = $^2$ =

Marks: /2

2. Find a number under 100 which is both a square and a cubed number.

Answer: Marks: /2

3. Which numbers between 1 and 30 have three factors?

Answer: Marks: /2

4. Abundant numbers occur when the sum of the factors of a number, not including itself, are greater than the number itself. For example, 12 is an abundant number, because its factors (not including itself), 1, 2, 3, 4 and 6, add up to 16. Complete your own investigation. You have two minutes to find as many abundant numbers under 100 as possible.

Answer: Marks: /2

## Super Sleuth challenge

Decide which labels from the list below you think this Venn diagram should include. Then, create your own Venn diagram puzzle using these labels.

| Prime Numbers | Composite Numbers |
|---|---|
| Odd Numbers | Even Numbers |
| Multiples of 3 | Square numbers |
| Factors of 64 | Between 7 and 28 |

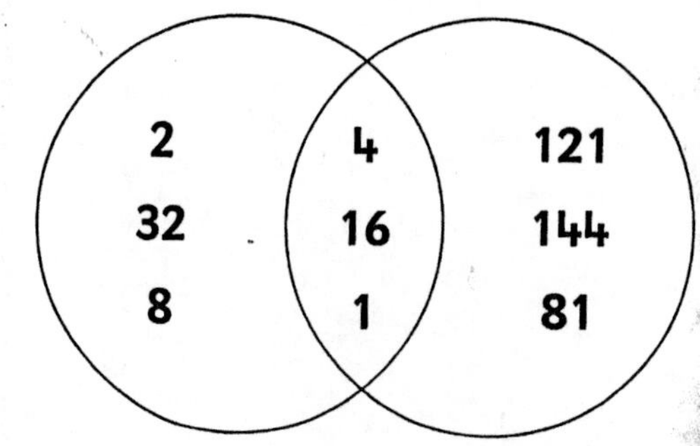




Today's Marks: /8

# 21 Number Theory

**We are learning to:** Identify simple prime and composite numbers. ▢ Identify and explore square and cubed numbers. ▢ Identify common factors and multiples. ▢

## Day One Try these.

1. Draw a diagram that represents $5^2$ and fill in the missing values based on your diagram.

$\_\_ \times \_\_ = \_\_^2 = \_\_$

Marks: /2

2. Find a number under 100 which is both a square and a cubed number.

Answer:

Marks: /2

3. Which numbers between 1 and 30 have three factors?

Answer:

Marks: /2

4. Abundant numbers occur when the sum of the factors of a number, not including itself, are greater than the number itself. For example, 12 is an abundant number, because its factors (not including itself), 1, 2, 3, 4 and 6, add up to 16. Complete your own investigation. You have two minutes to find as many abundant numbers under 100 as possible.

**Duties**

Answer:

Marks: /2

## Super Sleuth challenge

Decide which labels from the list below you think this Venn diagram should include. Then, create your own Venn diagram puzzle using these labels.

| Prime Numbers | Composite Numbers |
|---|---|
| Odd Numbers | Even Numbers |
| Multiples of 3 | Square numbers |
| Factors of 64 | Between 7 and 28 |

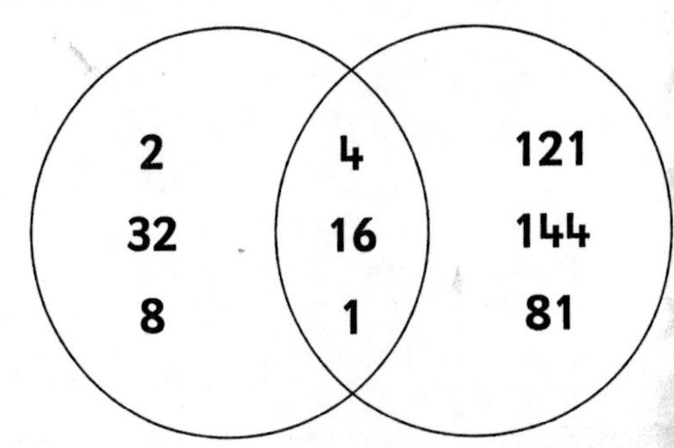




Today's Marks: /8

## Day Two Try these.

CLUES

1. Jenny thought of a number. She added 2 to it and squared it. She ended up with 81. Work backwards to work out the number that she started with.

**Answer:** **Marks:** /2

2. Jack multiplied a number by 16. The square root of Jack's new number was 8. What was the number Jack thought about at the start?

**Answer:** **Marks:** /2

3. I am a composite number. I have four factors, all of which are odd. I am an odd number too. The sum of my factors is 24. What number am I?

**Top tip:** Use trial and improvement.

**Answer:** **Marks:** /2

4. Using a calculator, try the following activity with five prime numbers no lower than 5: 

**Step 1** – Square your prime number (i.e. multiply your prime number by itself).

**Step 2** – Take away 1.

Once you have all five answers, look for a common link between them. Share your thoughts with your classmates.

**Top tip:** Work systematically.

**Answer:** **Marks:** /2

### Super Sleuth investigates

Use a calculator for this activity. 220 and 284 are amicable numbers. Follow these steps:

**Step 1** – F220 = ( , , , , , , , , , , , 220)

**Step 2** – Add the factors of 220. Don't include 220.

**Step 3** – F284 = ( , , , , , 284)

**Step 4** Add the factors of 284. Don't include 284.

What did you notice in this activity? Discuss your thoughts with a partner and share your definition of amicable numbers with your class.

**Today's Marks:** /8

## Day Three

Try these.

| Lowest Common Multiple | Highest Common Factor |
|---|---|
| **Step 1:** List the multiples of both numbers. | **Step 1:** List the factors of both numbers. |
| **Step 2:** Identify the lowest multiple that both numbers have in common. | **Step 2:** Identify the highest number that divides evenly into both numbers. |
| **Example:** Find the lowest common multiple of 3 and 4. Multiples of 3: 3, 6, 9, **12**, 15, 18 ... Multiples of 4: 4, 8, **12**, 16, 20 ... **Answer:** The lowest common multiple of 3 and 4 is 12. | **Example:** Find the highest common factor of 27 and 36. F27 = (1, 3, **9**, 27) F36 = (1, 2, 3, 4, 6, **9**, 12, 18, 36) **Answer:** While 27 and 36 have other common factors, 9 is the highest. |

1. Find the lowest common multiple of 20 and 25.

Answer: Marks: /2

2. What is the highest common factor of 16 and 32?

Answer: Marks: /2

3. Work out the lowest common multiple of 2, 9 and 12.

Answer: Marks: /2

4. Add the highest common factor of 15, 45 and 60 to $7^2$.

Answer: Marks: /2

### Puzzle power

All of the answers in today's tasks can be written in exponential form. Write these answers again, this time in exponential form.

**1.** $\square^2$ **2.** $\square^4$ **3.** $\square^2$ **4.** $\square^3$



Today's Marks: /8

## Day Four Try these.

1. When Super Sleuth adds three consecutive square numbers together, the answer is 110. What might those square numbers be?

Answer: Marks: /2

2. Super Sleuth investigated two square numbers with a difference of 17. What are those two square numbers?

Answer: Marks: /2

3. Super Sleuth has heard reports of a rival detective stating, "When you add two consecutive square numbers, you always get a prime number. The examples are 1 + 4 = 5 and 4 + 9 = 13." Prove whether this statement is right or wrong in the box below.

Marks: /2

4. Super Sleuth suspects that you can add two prime numbers together to get 64, but he needs your help to prove it. How many pairs of prime numbers can you think of that add up to 64?

Answer: Marks: /2

Today's Marks: /8

### Puzzle power

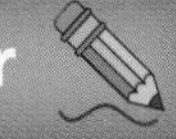

What have you learned in this unit that you could use to solve the following puzzle? Enda and Seán go to the gym regularly. Enda goes every five days, but Seán goes every three days. Their friend Luke goes to the gym every 9 days. If they all went to the gym together on April 12th, on what date will they all go to the gym together again?

Total Marks: /32 | I feel confident about

I would like to work on

# 22 Capacity

**We are learning to:** Add, subtract, multiply and divide litres and millilitres. ☐
Find the volume of a cuboid experimentally. ☐

## Day One

**Study the steps used to solve the problem in the example below.**

Declan's fish tank has a volume of 4.32 $m^3$. Find the width if the height is 1.2 m and the length is 2 m.

CLUES

**Circle the numbers and keywords:**
height is 1.2 m, length is 2 m, width is ?

**Link with operation needed (+, –, × or ÷):** Multiply (×). Divide (÷).

**Use a strategy:** Work backwards.

**Estimate and calculate:**
My estimate: less than 2 m

$1.2\text{ m} \times 2\text{ m} \times \square\text{ m} = 4.32\text{ m}^3$
$2.4\text{ m} \times \square\text{ m} = 4.32\text{ m}^3$
$4.32\text{ m}^3 \div 2.4\text{ m} = 1.8\text{ m}$

**Answer:** 1.8 m

**Summarise and check how you got your answer:**
I worked backwards to find the missing value.

### Try these.

CLUES

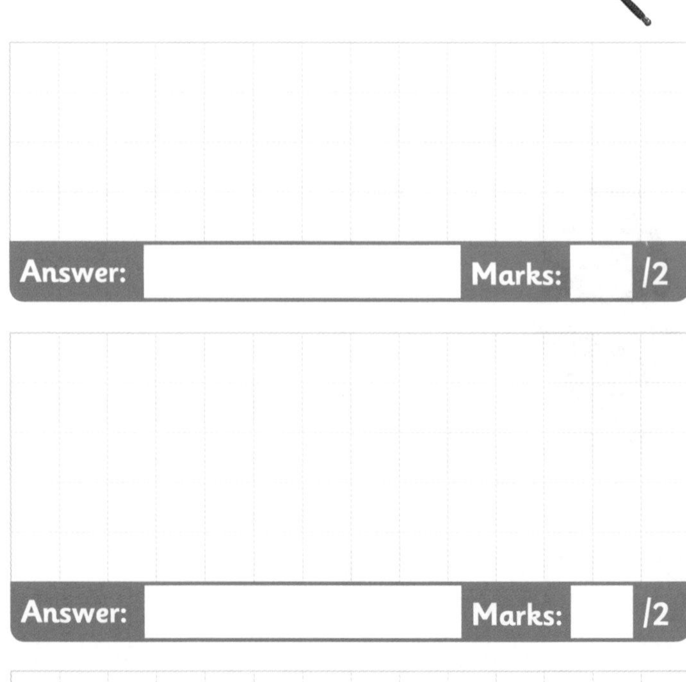

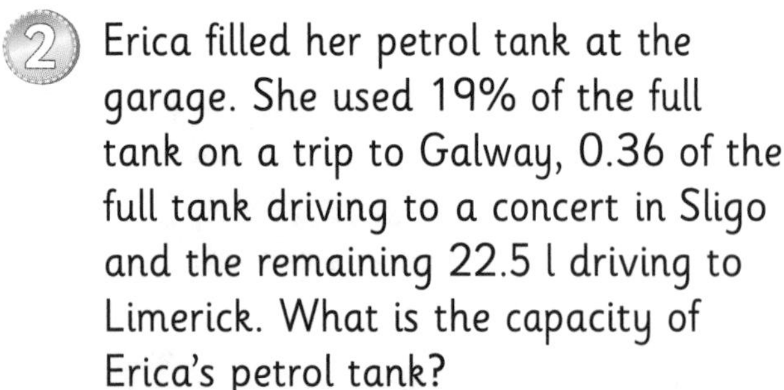

1. During a car journey, Erica shared a carton of juice between herself and her family. She gave 25% of it to her sister, $\frac{2}{5}$ of it to her cousin and $\frac{3}{20}$ of it to her father and kept the remaining 175 ml for herself. How much juice did Erica have to begin with?

   **Answer:** ____ **Marks:** ____ /2

2. Erica filled her petrol tank at the garage. She used 19% of the full tank on a trip to Galway, 0.36 of the full tank driving to a concert in Sligo and the remaining 22.5 l driving to Limerick. What is the capacity of Erica's petrol tank?

   **Answer:** ____ **Marks:** ____ /2

3. Based on the answer to question 2 above, if petrol costs €1.20 per litre, how much did it cost Erica to **(a)** fill her tank and **(b)** travel to Galway?

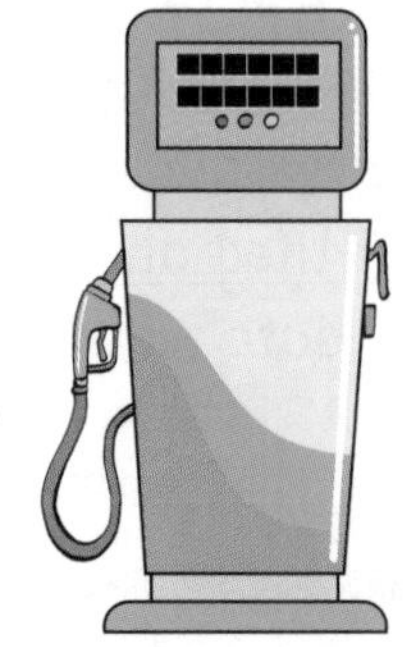

   **Answers: (a)** ____ **(b)** ____ **Marks:** ____ /4



**Today's Marks:** ____ /8

# Day Two Try these.

| $1\ ml = 0.001\ l = \frac{1}{1000}\ l$ | $10\ ml = 0.01\ l = \frac{1}{100}\ l$ |
|---|---|
| $100\ ml = 0.1\ l = \frac{1}{10}\ l$ | $1,000\ ml = 1\ l$ |

1. At Aqua Park, the capacity of the adults' swimming pool is 375,000 l. The pool is filled with 5 taps, all pumping the same amount of water into the pool. How many hours does it take to fill the pool if each tap pumps 25,000 l per hour?

**Answer:** **Marks:** /2

2. The children's pool is filled by 3 taps, each pumping 25,000 l of water into the pool per hour for 2 and a half hours. What is the capacity of this pool?

**Answer:** **Marks:** /2

3. (a) What is the combined capacity of the two pools at Aqua Park? (b) What is the difference in capacity between the two pools?

**Answers: (a)** **(b)** **Marks:** /4

4. If Aqua Park has to pay water charges to the council at a rate of 3c per 1,000 litres for the adults' pool and 1c per 500 litres for the children's pool, how much does it cost to fill both pools every day for a full week?

**Answer: €** **Marks:** /2

**Today's Marks:** /10

# Day Three Try these.

**Keywords**

The volume of a shape is the amount of space that it takes up. This can be measured in $mm^3$, $cm^3$, $m^3$ or $km^3$. To find the volume of a shape, we multiply length by width by height.

You will need 1 litre milk cartons today. Ask for an adult's help to cut a clean, empty milk carton to reveal its net. Is the net bigger or smaller than you expected?

## Super Sleuth investigates

Cut off one side of a 1 litre milk carton. Fill it with 1 $cm^3$ cubes.

1. How many cubes does it take to fill the carton?

   This is the volume of the container. It is measured in $cm^3$.

2. Describe the relationship between $cm^3$ and litres with your group.

**Duties**

Reader

Calculator

Checker

Reporter

**1** If we add two layers of cubes to the top of this shape, what will the volume of the new shape be?

**Top tip:** Each cube measures 1 $cm^3$.

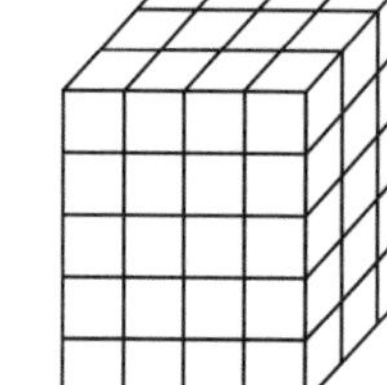

**Answer:** **Marks:** /2

**2** Use a calculator for these questions. **(a)** Ryanair has a size limit of 55 cm × 40 cm × 20 cm for carry-on baggage. What is the volume of a suitcase this size? **(b)** Iberia has a size limit of 56 cm × 45 cm × 25 cm for carry-on baggage. How much greater is this than the volume allowed by Ryanair?

**Answers: (a)** $cm^3$ **(b)** $cm^3$ **Marks:** /4

**3** The Dubai Aquarium tank in Dubai Mall has a volume of 11,220 $m^3$. If the height of the tank is 11 m and the width is 20 m, what is the length of the tank?

**Answer:** **Marks:** /2



**Today's Marks:** /8

# Day Four Try these.

1. Mum has lost some of her measuring jugs and asks you to pour exactly 75 ml of water into a glass. She gives you two measuring jugs: one with a capacity of 100 ml and another with a capacity of 85 ml. Is it possible to measure exactly 75 ml using these two jugs? If so, explain how you could do this.

Answer: Marks: /2

2. Next, Mum asks you to measure out exactly 4 litres using one jug with a capacity of 3 litres and another with a capacity of 5 litres. Explain how you could do this. (There is more than one answer.)

Answer: Marks: /2

3. If the area of one square face on this cuboid is 49 $cm^2$, what is the volume of this cuboid?

15 cm

Answer: $cm^3$ Marks: /2

Today's Marks: /6

## Super Sleuth investigates

In pairs, construct a container with the greatest capacity that you can make using an A4 sheet of paper and sticky tape. This should be a 3-D shape of your choice. To test the capacity, fill your container with non-standard units, e.g. cubes, beads or bags of rice. Record and compare your results with those of other pairs. Which container has the greatest/smallest capacity? What changes could you have made to your container to increase its capacity?

Total Marks: /32 | I am good at

I would like to get better at

# 23 Lines and Angles

**We are learning to:** Classify angles. ☐ Measure angles. ☐ Construct angles. ☐ Recognise angles in terms of a rotation. ☐

## Day One

Here is a reminder of the names of the different types of angle:

| Acute | Right | Obtuse | Straight | Reflex |
|---|---|---|---|---|
| Less than 90° | 90° | Greater than 90°, but less than 180° | 180° | Greater than 180° |

**Try these.**

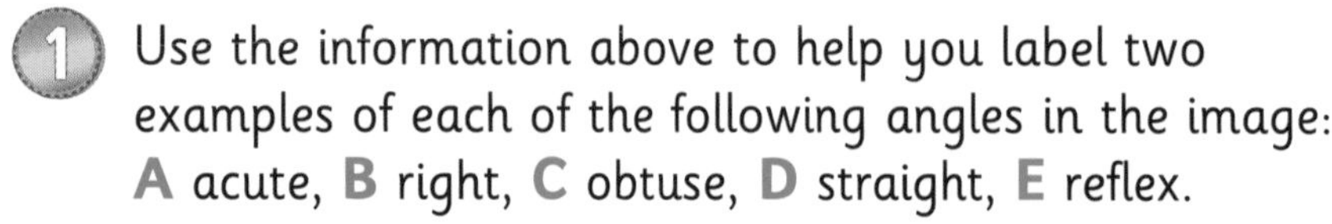

1. Use the information above to help you label two examples of each of the following angles in the image: **A** acute, **B** right, **C** obtuse, **D** straight, **E** reflex.

**Marks:** /10

**Top tip:** Always ensure that you estimate the size of an angle before you measure. If your measurement is completely different to your estimate, you should check if you used the correct scale on your protractor.

2. Fill in the table below based on the image.

| Angle | Estimate | Measurement | Type of Angle |
|---|---|---|---|
| A | | | |
| B | | | |
| C | | | |
| D | | | |
| E | | | |
| F | | | |

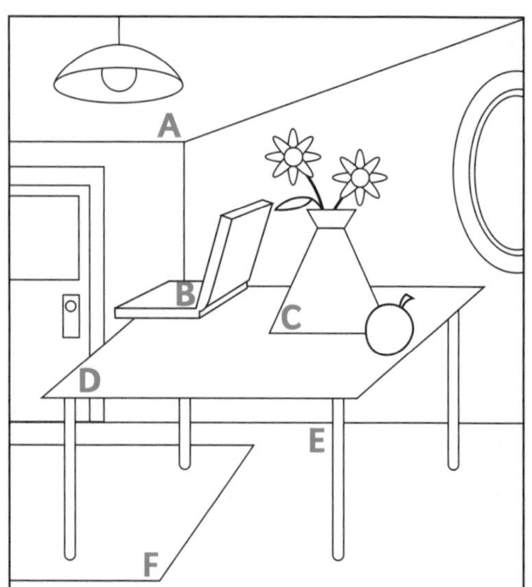


**Marks:** /12

# Day Two Try these.

CLUES

## Constructing Angles

Here are four simple steps to follow when drawing an angle:

1. Draw a line and make a mark at one end of the line.
2. Place the base line of your protractor on the line you have drawn, ensuring that the centre point is on the mark you made.
3. Count from 0° to the angle you would like to construct. Mark this point.
4. Now, join both of your marks using a ruler. You have made your angle!

1. In your copy, use a ruler to draw a picture of your favourite room in your home. Label five different types of angle in your picture. **Marks: /2**

2. There are only 180° on a protractor. How could you construct an angle of 305°? Test your idea in the box below.

**Marks: /2**

3. In your copy, recreate the drawing below. Use a ruler and a protractor to ensure that you use the exact measurements shown. You can change the scale if you like.

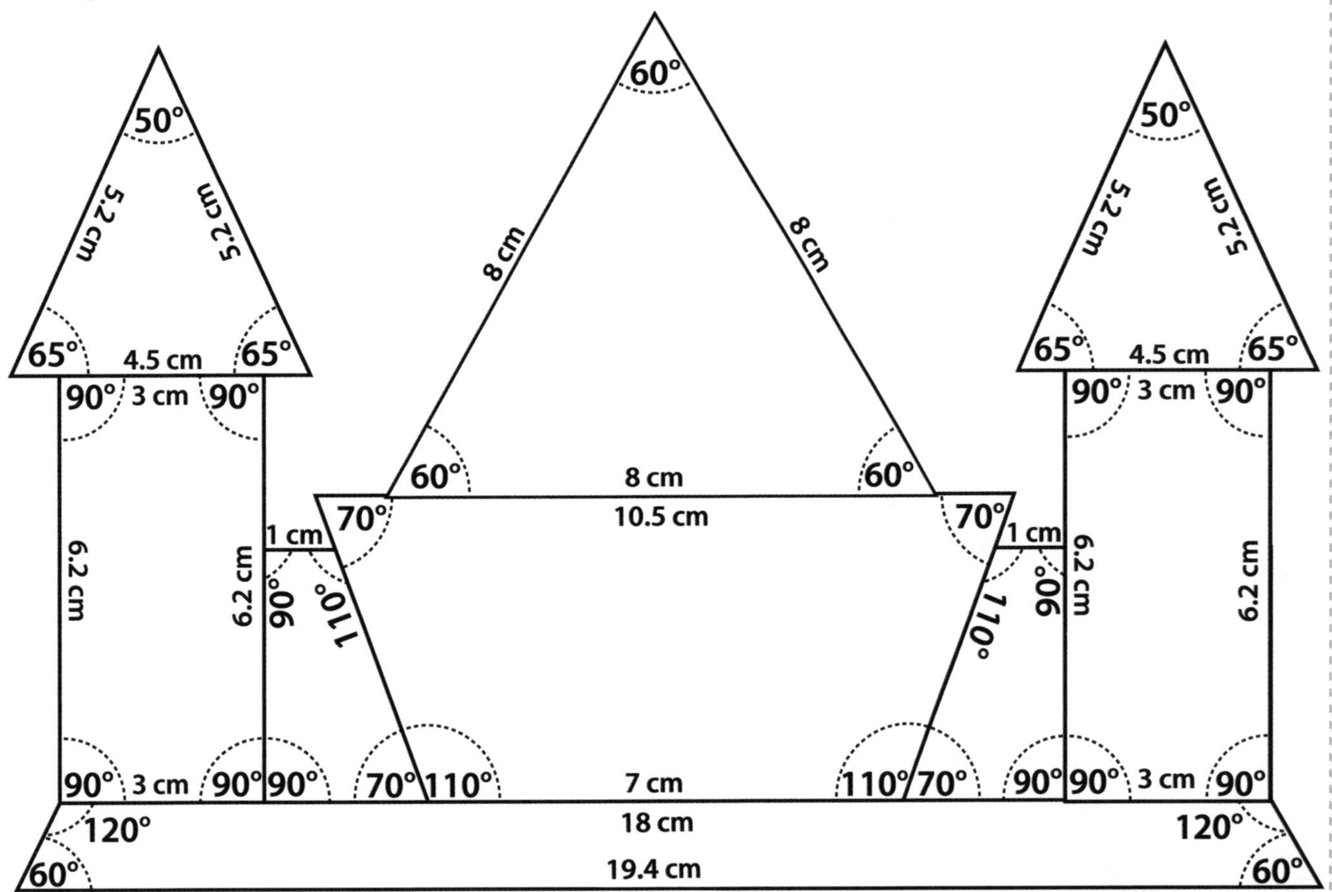


**Marks: /2**

## Day Three

Try these.

CLUES

### Spin 'n' Win

The spinner moves in a clockwise direction.

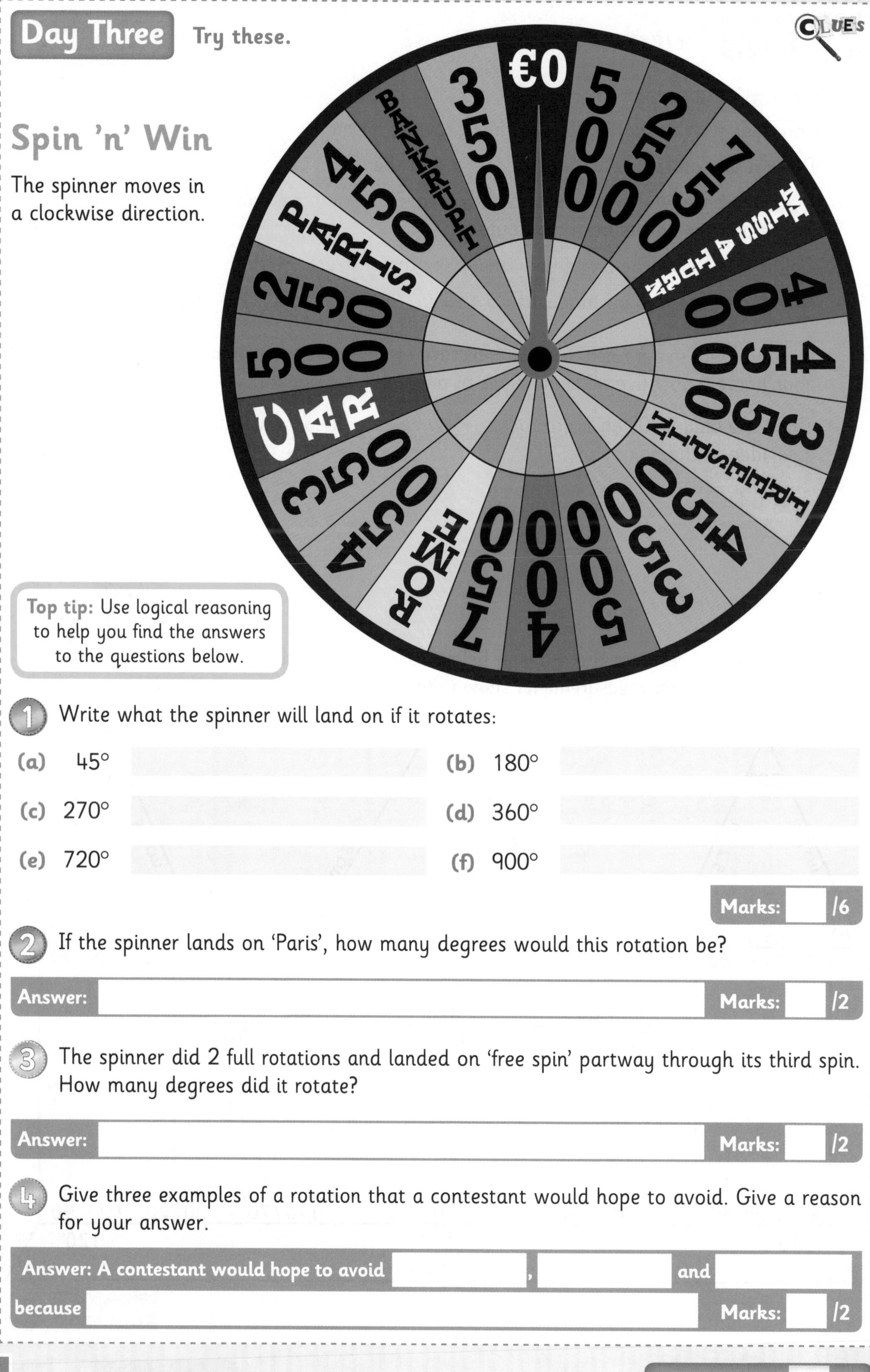


**Top tip:** Use logical reasoning to help you find the answers to the questions below.

1. Write what the spinner will land on if it rotates:

(a) 45° ______ (b) 180° ______

(c) 270° ______ (d) 360° ______

(e) 720° ______ (f) 900° ______

**Marks:** /6

2. If the spinner lands on 'Paris', how many degrees would this rotation be?

**Answer:** ______ **Marks:** /2

3. The spinner did 2 full rotations and landed on 'free spin' partway through its third spin. How many degrees did it rotate?

**Answer:** ______ **Marks:** /2

4. Give three examples of a rotation that a contestant would hope to avoid. Give a reason for your answer.

**Answer: A contestant would hope to avoid** ______, ______ **and** ______ **because** ______ **Marks:** /2



**Today's Marks:** /12

# Day Four Try these.

In pairs, take turns estimating the size of the angles in the shapes below.

- In round 1, Contestant A starts by estimating the size of the acute angle, while Contestant B estimates the size of the reflex angle. Both contestants must then measure the angles together and agree on the final measurements.
- In round 2, Contestant A estimates the size of the reflex angle, while Contestant B estimates the size of the acute angle and so on, continuing to swap acute and reflex angles until you have completed rounds 3 and 4.
- The winner is the contestant with the smallest overall difference between their estimates and actual answers. Good luck!

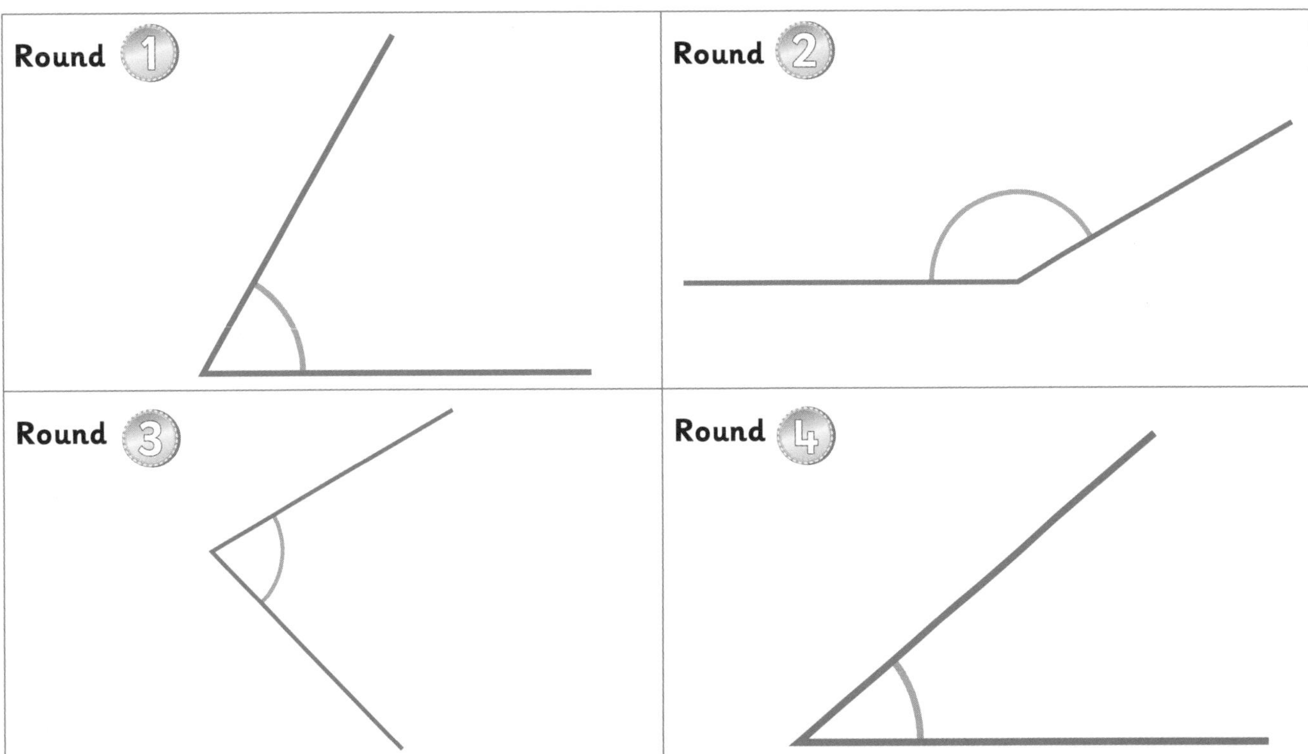


| Contestant A | | | |
|---|---|---|---|
| | Estimate | Measurement | Difference |
| Round 1 | | | |
| Round 2 | | | |
| Round 3 | | | |
| Round 4 | | | |
| | | | |

| Contestant B | | | |
|---|---|---|---|
| | Estimate | Measurement | Difference |
| Round 1 | | | |
| Round 2 | | | |
| Round 3 | | | |
| Round 4 | | | |
| | | | |

Today's Marks: /8

Total Marks: /48 | I can use a protractor to measure angles. Yes No

I can use a protractor and a ruler to construct angles. Yes No

# 24 Revision 4

## Day One Try these.

1. Tara looked at the time and saw that it was 01:23. She noticed that the numbers were in consecutive order. Can you think of two other examples of a time with numbers in consecutive order on a 24-hour clock?

**Answer:** **Marks:** /2

2. Yanick is allowed to play on the Xbox for 45 minutes at a time, but must take a break of 20 minutes. He played 3 sessions on the Xbox and took two breaks. If he started at 4:15 pm, at what time did he finish playing on the Xbox?

**Answer:** **Marks:** /2

3. A NASA spacecraft travelled a distance of 386,352 km to the moon. If the spacecraft travelled at the same speed for 3 full days, at how many kilometres per hour did it travel?

**Answer:** **Marks:** /2

4. Work out which activity each child is most likely to be doing based on the local time in their city. The time difference is in brackets after each city.

| Child | City | Time | Activity |
|---|---|---|---|
| **Sharon** | Dublin | 8:40 pm | Watching television with her parents |
| **Rob** | Los Angeles (–8 hours) | | |
| **Camila** | Buenos Aires (–4 hours) | | |
| **Nina** | Manila (+7 hours) | | |
| **Jackson** | Auckland (+11 hours) | | |

Eating breakfast

At school

Sleeping

Eating dinner

**Marks:** /2



Strand: Number Strand Unit: Number Theory Strand: Measures Strand Units: Time; Capacity
Strand: Shape and Space Strand Unit: Lines and Angles

**Today's Marks:** /8

## Day Two Try these.

CLUES

1. Find the product of $3^4$ and $2^6$.

**Answer:** **Marks:** /2

2. **(a)** Work out which is greater: the sum of the first five prime numbers starting at 3 or the sum of the first five composite numbers starting at 4. **(b)** What is the difference between them?

**Answers: (a)** **(b)** **Marks:** /2

3. **(a)** Work out which is greater: the sum of the first five multiples of 4 or the sum of the first six multiples of 3. **(b)** What is the difference between them?

**Answers: (a)** **(b)** **Marks:** /2

4. The school bells in Greensdale Senior School, Greensdale Junior School and Greensdale Secondary School ring at intervals of 10, 25 and 40 minutes.
If the bells all ring at 9:05 am, what is the next time at which they will all ring together?

**Answer:** **Marks:** /2

### Puzzle power

Lexie has thought of two numbers. Their highest common factor is 6. Their lowest common multiple is 36. What numbers might Lexie be thinking of?

**Today's Marks:** /8

## Day Three Try these.

CLUES

1. Mikel gave $\frac{3}{10}$ l of juice to Leona, $\frac{1}{5}$ l each to Pippa and Cassie and 150 ml to Melinda. If Mikel had 135 ml of juice left, how much did he have to begin with?

Answer: Marks: /2

2. Pat's lunch box has a volume of 2,688 $cm^3$. If the width of the lunch box is 14 cm and the height is 8 cm, would it be long enough to fit a hot dog that is 29 cm long? It cannot be placed diagonally in the lunch box.

**Top tip:** Work backwards.

Answer: Marks: /2

3. This puzzle is tricky and may take longer than usual to solve. Jane has three bottles of fizzy drinks: Bitter Lemonade, Strawberry Delight and Pineapple Perfection. The Bitter Lemonade and Strawberry Delight bottles have a combined capacity of 3.15 l. The Strawberry Delight and Pineapple Perfection bottles have a combined capacity of 2.25 l. The Bitter Lemonade and Pineapple Perfection bottles have a combined capacity of 2.8 l. Can you work out the capacity of each bottle?

**Duties**

BL + SD = 3.15 l
SD + PP = 2.25 l
BL + PP = 2.8 l

**Top tip:** Use trial and improvement. Try different values for each of the bottles. For each guess, keep 'BL' the same value, 'SD the same value and so on. Keep trying until the number sentences all make sense.

**Top tip:** The answers are all between 0.9 l and 1.90 l.

Answer: BL = SD = PP = Marks: /3



Today's Marks: /7

## Day Four Try these.

CLUES

1. Draw a diagram showing how much time passes when the minute hand of a clock rotates 270°.

**Top tip:**
When the minute hand travels 5 minutes, this is a rotation of 30°.

Marks: /1

2. The rotors of a wind turbine make 6 whole revolutions in one minute. How many degrees do the rotors rotate in one hour?

Answer: Marks: /2

3. Draw an angle of 295°.

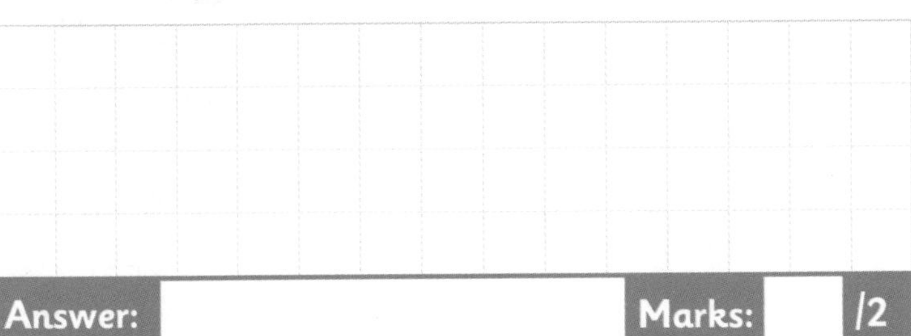


Marks: /2

4. Calculate the missing angles in this triangle. This puzzle is a little different. Take your time working out the value of the second angle and use this information to find the value of the third angle.

330°

Answer: Marks: /2

Today's Marks: /7

### Super Sleuth challenge

Write the name of your school in block capital letters. Identify and label the various angles that you can find in each letter.

# 25 Strategy: Working Systematically

## Day One

Working systematically involves organising the data that you have and building on it until you find your answer. It might involve making a list, drawing a diagram, making a table or exploring a puzzle with many possible answers.

**Example:** Erin paid for a new dress costing €60 with an equal number of €5 and €10 notes. With how many of each type of note did she pay for the dress?

Making a table will help you to organise the information in a way that is clear to see and easy to understand.

| No. of notes | €5 | €10 | Total |
|---|---|---|---|
| 1 | €5 | €10 | €15 |
| 2 | €10 | €20 | €30 |
| 3 | €15 | €30 | €45 |
| 4 | €20 | €40 | €60 |

**Answer:** Erin paid for the dress with four €5 notes and four €10 notes.

### Try these.

CLUES

1. Kalinda has 9 cubes in a bag: 3 red, 3 blue and 3 yellow. If she pulls out 4 cubes, what combinations of colours might she have? Write as many possible outcomes as you can in the box below.

Marks: /2

2. Be a fact checker! Super Sleuth has heard a rumour that if you double the length of the sides of a square, the area will double in size too. Super Sleuth doesn't quite believe this and needs your help! In your copy, draw three squares and see for yourself what happens to the area when you double the length of the sides.
Measure the sides. Record your findings in the table below.

| Original Sides | Area |
|---|---|
| | |
| | |
| | |

| Sides Doubled | New Area |
|---|---|
| | |
| | |
| | |

Marks: /3

3. In question 2, did you notice a pattern? What do you think happens to the area of a square when you double the length of the sides?

Answer:

Marks: /2



Today's Marks: /7

## Day Two Try these.

1. Ria, Emilia and Innez are best friends and all love swimming. Ria visits the swimming pool every 5 days, Emilia visits every 2 days and Innez visits every 3 days. If the three friends are all in the swimming pool today, after how many days will they be back in the swimming pool together?

Answer: Marks: /2

2. Ciaran, Alex and Ross love playing Xbox Live together online. Ciaran's mother allows him to play every 3 days and Alex is allowed to play every 4 days, but poor Ross is only allowed to play every 7 days. If the boys are all playing Xbox Live today, in how many days' time will they all play together again?

Answer: Marks: /2

3. Using the information in question 2, if Ciaran, Alex and Ross were all playing Xbox Live on June 17th, on what date will all three boys play together again?

Answer: Marks: /2

4. Ross paid for his newest Xbox game with an equal number of €2 and 50c coins. If the game cost €77.50, with how many of each type of coin did he pay?

**Top tip:** In pairs, plan how you will solve this puzzle before you begin.

Answer: Marks: /2

Today's Marks: /8

## Day Three Try these.

1. There are 85 houses in Shona's estate. Use the following clues to work out the number of her house:

- It is not a multiple of 5.
- It is not a square number.
- It has double digits.
- It is a prime number.
- The units digit is larger than the tens digit.
- The number is a factor of 158.
- When you add the two digits together, you get a square number.

| 1 | 2 | 3 | 4 | 5 | 6 | 7 | 8 | 9 | 10 |
|---|---|---|---|---|---|---|---|---|---|
| 11 | 12 | 13 | 14 | 15 | 16 | 17 | 18 | 19 | 20 |
| 21 | 22 | 23 | 24 | 25 | 26 | 27 | 28 | 29 | 30 |
| 31 | 32 | 33 | 34 | 35 | 36 | 37 | 38 | 39 | 40 |
| 41 | 42 | 43 | 44 | 45 | 46 | 47 | 48 | 49 | 50 |
| 51 | 52 | 53 | 54 | 55 | 56 | 57 | 58 | 59 | 60 |
| 61 | 62 | 63 | 64 | 65 | 66 | 67 | 68 | 69 | 70 |
| 71 | 72 | 73 | 74 | 75 | 76 | 77 | 78 | 79 | 80 |
| 81 | 82 | 83 | 84 | 85 | | | | | |

**Answer:** ______ **Marks:** ___ /2

2. Jake lives in the same estate as Shona. Use the following clues to work out the number of his house:

- The number is between 10 and 45.
- It is an odd number.
- It is a composite number.
- The tens digit is smaller than the units digit.
- It is a multiple of 7.

| 10 | 11 | 12 | 13 | 14 | 15 |
|---|---|---|---|---|---|
| 16 | 17 | 18 | 19 | 20 | 21 |
| 22 | 23 | 24 | 25 | 26 | 27 |
| 28 | 29 | 30 | 31 | 32 | 33 |
| 34 | 35 | 36 | 37 | 38 | 39 |
| 40 | 41 | 42 | 43 | 44 | 45 |

**Answer:** ______ **Marks:** ___ /2

3. At the ice-cream van, Shona paid for an ice-cream cone and 2 packets of crisps with an equal number of 5c, 10c and 20c coins. If the treats cost €3.15, with how many of each type of coin did she pay?

**Answer:** ______ **Marks:** ___ /2

4. Jake spent the same amount of money as Shona at the ice-cream van. He paid with a €5 note and his change was made up of coins no bigger than 50c, but no smaller than 5c. What is **(a)** the fewest number and **(b)** largest number of coins that he could have received in change?

**Answer: (a)** ___ **(b)** ___ **Marks:** ___ /2

**Today's Marks:** ___ /8

# Day Four Try these.

1. How many different five-letter palindromic words can you make from the letters 'CYROTFDEAIMLNVK'? You can use each letter more than once.

**Answers:**

**Marks:** /2

2. The sum of Cal's parents' ages is 85. His dad is 3 years older than his mum. When Cal's age is added to their ages, the total is 96. How old will they each be when their combined age is 114?

**Answers:** Cal | Dad | Mum | **Marks:** /3

3. There are four children in the Byrne family: Ethan, Aidan, Sadie and Clara. They share their time on the iPad equally. There are 4 time slots per day for five days. The children do not have the same time slot on two consecutive days. Ethan doesn't want the iPad at 3:30 pm on Mondays and Sadie doesn't like to miss her favourite television programme on Fridays at 6:30 pm. Make a roster so that the children will be happy.

| | 3.30–4:00 pm | 4:30–5:00 pm | 5:30–6:00 pm | 6:30–7:00 pm |
|---|---|---|---|---|
| **Monday** | | | | |
| **Tuesday** | | | | |
| **Wednesday** | | | | |
| **Thursday** | | | | |
| **Friday** | | | | |

**Marks:** /4

**Today's Marks:** /9

## Super Sleuth challenge

**Duties**

Reader
Calculator
Checker
Reporter

You have been asked to create a new flag for your school. You can use up to five different colours. Each of the strips must be shaded in one colour only. As a group, create as many variations of the flag as you can. Think of a way to share the workload fairly between the members of the group.

**Total Marks:** /32 | **This is how I would explain to a friend what working systematically means:**

**There is just one thing I would like to know:**

# 26 Chance

**We are learning to:** Create frequency charts. ☐ Estimate the likelihood of occurrence of events using fractions and percentages. ☐ Identify and list all possible outcomes of simple random processes. ☐

## Day One

**Study the steps used to solve the problem in the example below.**

Kevin orders a 12-slice pizza special. It has 6 slices with pepperoni, 2 slices with chicken, 1 slice with ham and 3 slices with meatballs. If there is a power cut just before he opens the box, what is the likelihood that he will pick up a slice with meatballs?

**Circle the numbers and keywords:** 12, 3, likelihood

**Link with operation needed (+, −, × or ÷):** None

**Use a strategy:** Simplify and use logical reasoning.

**Estimate and calculate:**

| My estimate: This is less than half of the pizza. | 3 out of every 12 slices have meatballs. Simplify: 1 in 4 = $\frac{1}{4}$ = 25% = 0.25 | **Answer:** There is a 1 in 4 chance. |
|---|---|---|

**Summarise and check how you got your answer:**
I simplified 3 in 12 to become 1 in 4.

### Try these.

1. Find the probability of selecting a county on the island of Ireland that is in Leinster. Write your answer in its lowest terms.

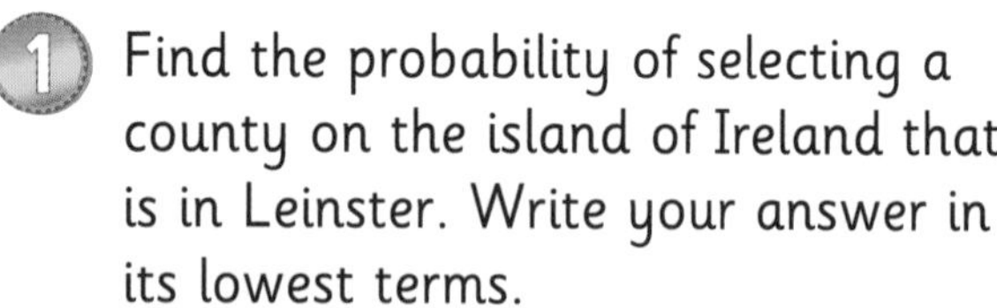

**Answer:** ______ **Marks:** ___ /2

2. Find the probability of selecting a county on the island of Ireland with three syllables in its name. Write your answer as a percentage.

**Answer:** ______ **Marks:** ___ /2

3. Find the probability of selecting a county in Ulster that is in Northern Ireland. Write your answer as a fraction and a percentage.

**Answer:** ______ **Marks:** ___ /2

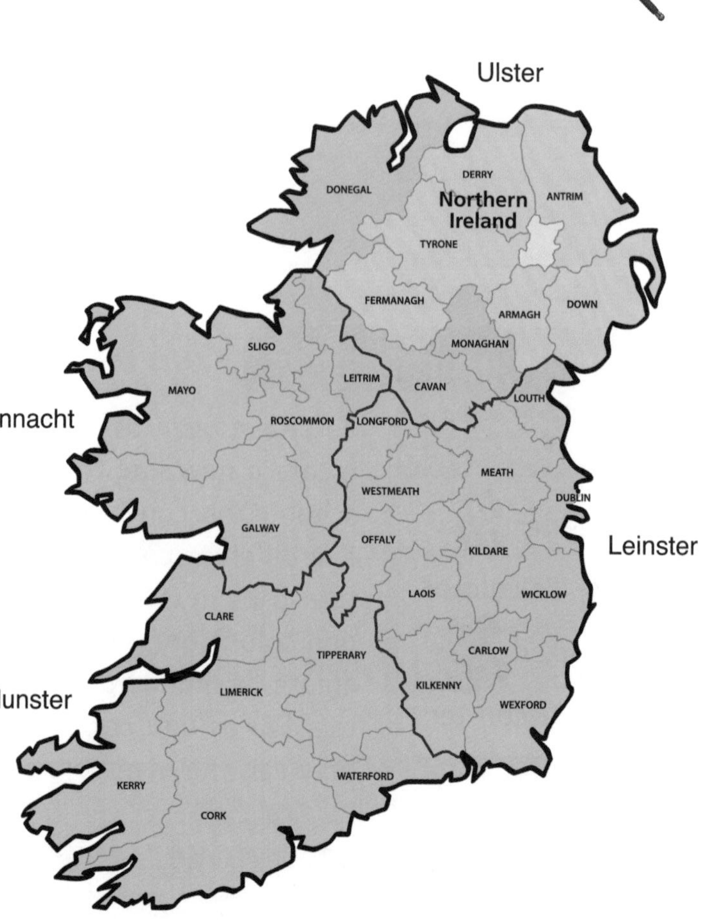




**Today's Marks:** ___ /6

## Day Two Try these.

CLUES

1. What are the chances of landing on a slot greater than 400 or a holiday?

Answer: ______ Marks: ___ /2

2. What are the chances of landing on a slot with words? Write your answer in fraction and percentage form.

Answer: ______ Marks: ___ /2

3. The wise owl has organised a fun activity for her friends the lion, the hare, the frog and the tortoise. They have to complete a 200 m race, with the owl rolling a die to decide whose turn it is to move forwards as follows:

- Every time the number 1 is rolled, the lion can run 50 m.
- Every time an even number is rolled, the frog can leap 60% as far as the lion can run.
- Every time an odd number is rolled, the hare can sprint $\frac{5}{6}$ of the frog's distance.
- Every time the numbers 2 or 5 are rolled, the tortoise can stroll 80% as far as the lion can run.

Which animal do you think will cross the finish line **(a)** first and **(b)** last? Give reasons for your answers.

**Duties**
Reader
Calculator
Checker
Reporter

**Top tip:**
Work systematically.

Answers: (a) ______
(b) ______ Marks: ___ /2

In groups try it out using a die to see which animal will win.

| Animal | Distance Travelled |
|---|---|
| Lion | |
| Frog | |
| Hare | |
| Tortoise | |

Finish line

Today's Marks: ___ /6

## Day Three Try these.

1. Draw 12 contestants in a car race. There are five different colour cars in the race. There is a 25% chance that red will win. There is a 1 in 6 chance that black will win. There is a 33 $\frac{1}{3}$% chance that green will win. Two of the cars are orange. The remaining cars are yellow. What are the chances that a yellow car will win? Write your answer as a fraction.

**Answer:** **Marks:** /2

2. What are the chances that a green or black car will win the race in question 1? Write your answer in fraction and percentage form.

**Answer:** **Marks:** /2

3. In groups of four, sit in a circle. Take off your shoes and place them in the middle of the circle in no particular order. Each pupil in the group must take a turn closing their eyes and picking up a shoe in each hand 25 times. Each pupil in the group must also take a turn recording the outcome of this investigation in their frequency chart below, so that when you combine your tallies at the end, you will get a result out of 100.

**Duties**

Reader
Calculator
Checker
Reporter

**Frequency Chart**

| Outcome | Tally | Total |
|---|---|---|
| Left and left | | |
| Right and right | | |
| Right and left | | |

**Keywords**

A **frequency chart** is a table used to record how often something happens.

Using the results in the frequency chart, complete the following statements:

- The chances of picking up two left shoes are ______ in 100.
- The chances of picking up two right shoes are ______ in 100.
- The chances of picking up a left shoe and a right shoe are ______ in 100.

Compare and discuss your results with those of other groups.

**Marks:** /2



**Today's Marks:** /6

## Day Four Try these.

1. Nine consecutive coin tosses have resulted in heads winning. What are the chances of the 10th coin toss revealing heads?

Answer: | Marks: /1

2. Write three questions linked to chance that you could ask about the image below. Write the answer to each of your questions.

(a)

Answer:

(b)

Answer:

(c)

Answer:

Marks: /3

3. Write a question that could only be answered with the following: **(a)** likely or unlikely, **(b)** never or definitely.

(a)

(b)

Marks: /2

Today's Marks: /6

### Super Sleuth investigates

Think of a question that people can only give a 'yes' or 'no' answer to. Predict how you think your classmates would answer. Survey your classmates and record the results in a frequency chart.

| Frequency Chart | | |
|---|---|---|
| **Outcome** | **Tally** | **Total** |
| Yes | | |
| No | | |

Total Marks: /24 | I now fully understand what chance means in maths. Yes ☐ No ☐

I can make a frequency chart. Yes ☐ No ☐

# 27  3-D Shapes

**We are learning to:** Draw nets of 3-D shapes. ☐ Identify 3-D shapes from their nets. ☐ Construct 3-D shapes. ☐

## Day One Try these.

CLUES

**1** Mr Smart was organising resources for his class on 3-D shapes. When he found the nets, he discovered that they had been cut in two! Can you help him to match the halves of the nets?

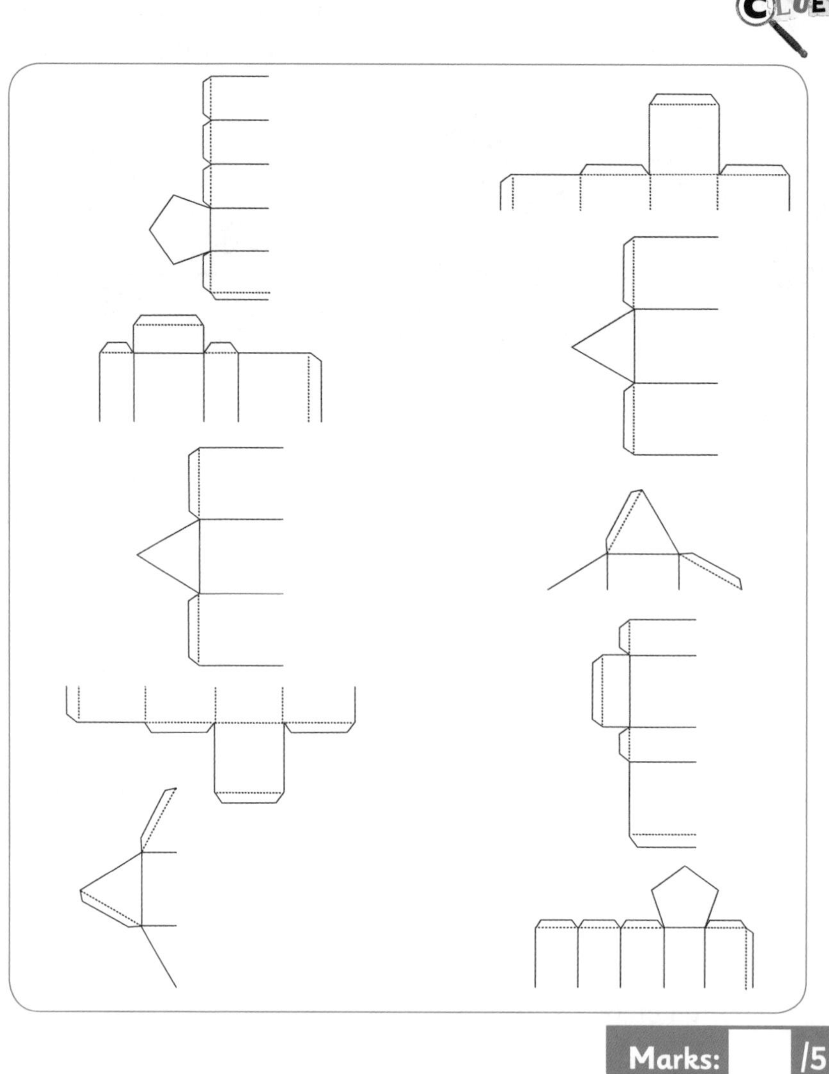

**Keywords**

A **net** is a pattern that you can cut and fold to make a model of a 3-D shape.

**Marks: /5**

**2** Draw the complete nets that you matched above. Label each net with the 3-D shape that it will make.

| | | | | |
|---|---|---|---|---|
| | | | | |
| | | | | |

**Marks: /10**

**3** Construct each of the 3-D shapes above using the nets to help you.

## Day Two Try these.

| Planets of the Solar System | | | |
|---|---|---|---|
| **Planet** | **Diameter** | **Radius** | **Circumference** |
| **Mercury** | 4,878 km | | 15,329 km |
| **Venus** | | 6,052 km | 38,025 km |
| **Earth** | 12,756 km | | 40,075 km |
| **Mars** | 6,794 km | | 21,343 km |
| **Jupiter** | | 71,492 km | 439,264 km |
| **Saturn** | | 60,268 km | 366,035 km |
| **Uranus** | 51,118 km | | 159,354 km |
| **Neptune** | | 24,764 km | 155,600 km |

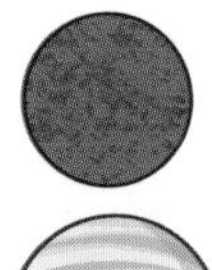
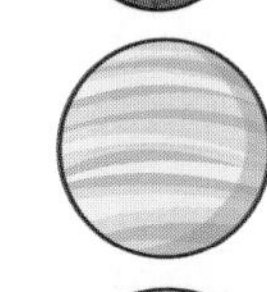

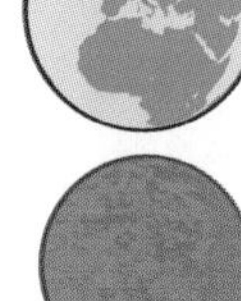

1. Work out and fill in the missing diameter and radius values in the table above.

**Marks:** /8

2. Identify the planet with **(a)** the largest diameter and circumference and **(b)** the smallest diameter and circumference.

**Answers: (a)** ____ **(b)** ____ **Marks:** /2

3. Using the example shown, **(a)** construct one cube, **(b)** a tower of three cubes and **(c)** another configuration of four cubes.

**Marks:** /3

**Today's Marks:** /13

## Day Three Try these.

1. I am a 3-D shape with twelve edges, seven vertices and seven faces. Six of my faces are identical. Name my shape!

**Answer:** **Marks:** /1

2. I am a 3-D shape with twelve edges, six vertices and eight faces. My faces are all identical. Name my shape!

**Answer:** **Marks:** /1

3. I am a 3-D shape. You could cut me into equal slices, but I am **not** a prism. I have three faces, two of which are identical. Name my shape!

**Answer:** **Marks:** /1

4. I am a 3-D shape with six edges, four vertices and four faces. All of my sides are identical. Name my shape!

**Answer:** **Marks:** /1

### Super Sleuth challenge

Create two 'name my shape' riddles of your own. You can use items in your classroom to help with your choices. Swap with a partner and solve each other's riddles.

### Super Sleuth investigates

1. Making models is a good way to investigate 3-D shapes. Use your knowledge to construct the 3-D shapes in the questions above and present them to your class.
2. Construct your favourite television or film character using a minimum of four 3-D shapes. Plan how you will construct your character in the box provided. Label the shapes that you will use. Describe your character to a partner and remember to say how many faces, edges and vertices it will have.



**Today's Marks:** /4

# Day Four Try these.

1. Super Sleuth's rival detective believes that each of these nets will make a cube. Do you agree? Justify your answer with an explanation.

**A**

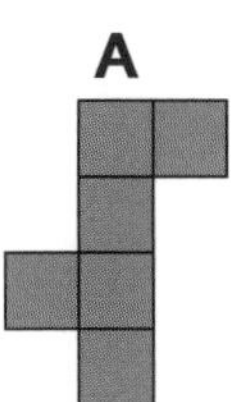

**B**

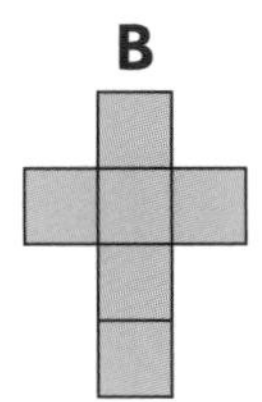

**C**

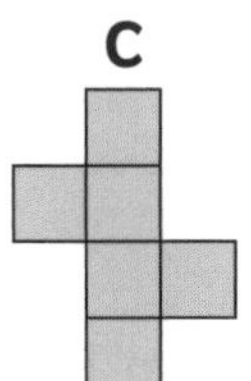

**D**

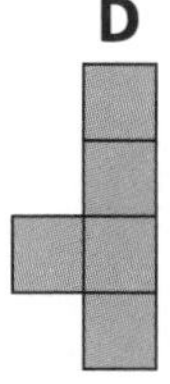

**Answer:** Marks: /2

2. Draw an octahedron on the isometric dots.

Many professionals use isometric drawings in their work. Can you think of any jobs that might require the use of this type of paper?

Marks: /2

3. Here are three views of a die on which the word 'SLEUTH' is written. Can you fill in the net to show how the letters would be arranged on the die?

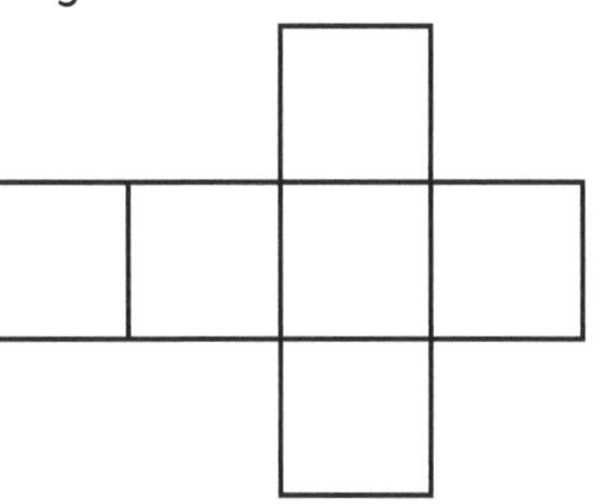

**Top tip:** Act it out.

Marks: /2

Today's Marks: /6

## Super Sleuth investigates

An anchor chart displays information about a topic in an attractive way. Create an anchor chart based on one 3-D shape. Your chart should include:

- The name of your shape.
- Facts such as the number of faces, vertices and edges in your shape.
- An image of the net of your shape.
- A model of your shape attached to the chart.

Present your chart to the class and talk about it for one minute.

Total Marks: /38 My favourite activity in this unit was ,

because

My least favourite activity in this chapter was

# 28  Directed Numbers

**We are learning to:** Use numbers greater than and less than zero. ☐
Add simple positive and negative numbers on the number line. ☐

## Day One

'Directed numbers' is the umbrella term for numbers that can be both negative and positive. Examples include –3, +17 and –1.8. It is a good idea to draw a number line to help answer questions. This will help you to visualise your work.

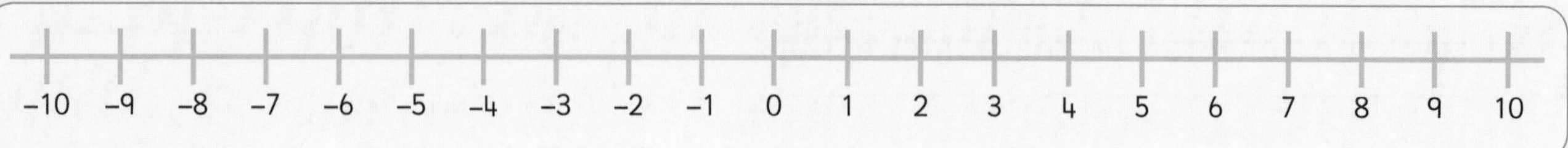


**Try these.**

 **(a)** Below is the control panel in a lift on a cruise ship. Do you notice anything unusual about the decks? This is not a mistake. Why do you think this is so? **(b)** How many decks are there on this cruise ship?

**Answers: (a)** ______ **(b)** ______ **Marks:** /2

- **Deck 14: Sunshine**
- **Deck 13: Sanctuary**
- **Deck 12: Poolside**
- **Deck 11: Food Court**
- **Deck 10: Stars**
- **Deck 9: Skyline**
- **Deck 8: Sports Centre**
- **Deck 7: Theatre**
- **Deck 6: Ocean Way**
- **Deck 5: Riviera**
- **Deck 4: Aloha**
- **Deck 3: Baja**
- **Deck 2: Café**
- **Deck 1: Shopping District**
- **Ground: Mall**
- **Deck –1: Relaxation**
- **Deck –2: Fiesta**
- **Deck –3: Plaza**
- **Deck –4: Gala**

2. Leon wants to attend a party on the Fiesta deck. Currently, he is eating a meal in the Food Court. How many floors below the Food Court is the Fiesta deck?

**Answer:** ______ **Marks:** /2

3. Nick can climb the stairs between the decks in 15 seconds. If he starts on the Gala deck, what deck will he be on after climbing for 135 seconds?

**Answer:** ______ **Marks:** /2

4. Sonny leaves his room on the Plaza deck and travels up 17 decks. He then travels down 18 decks before going up 16 decks. What do you think he will do here?

**Answer:** ______ **Marks:** /2



**Today's Marks:** /8

## Day Two Try these.

Look at Naoise's bank statement.

**Top tip:**
The amounts in the debit section are taken out of the account. Any amounts in the credit section are paid into the account.

| Date | Description | Debit | Credit | Balance |
|---|---|---|---|---|
| May 1st | Opening Balance | | | €25.00 |
| May 3rd | Gina's Gift Shop | €15.75 | | €9.25 |
| May 6th | Lodgement | | €65.00 | |
| May 11th | iTunes store | €4.50 | | |
| May 15th | Netflix | €9.99 | | |
| May 19th | Aer Lingus | €99.00 | | |
| May 20th | Lodgement | | €100.00 | |
| May 25th | Hollister | €74.50 | | |
| May 25th | Penneys | €21.25 | | |
| May 25th | Tesco | €18.46 | | |
| May 27th | Lodgement | | €20.00 | |
| May 31st | GameStop | €15.55 | | |

1. Fill in the missing balances in Naoise's bank statement.

**Marks:** /10

2. Was Naoise sensible with her money? Yes ☐ No ☐ Give a reason for your answer.

**Answer:**

**Marks:** /2

3. On what date did Naoise spend the most money?

**Answer:** **Marks:** /2

4. Payment for Naoise's phone bill will be taken out of her account on June 1st. If the bill is for €44.50, how much money will she have to lodge into her account to ensure that there is enough for the payment?

**Answer:** **Marks:** /2

**Today's Marks:** /16

## Day Three Try these.

| Player | Score | Strokes |
|---|---|---|
| F. Fahey | –1 | 73 |
| O. Ryan | +4 | |
| C. Jordan | –2 | |
| A. Curley | +7 | |
| E. Smith | –5 | |

Woodview Golf Course is a par 74. This means that a golfer should hit the golf ball 74 times to complete the course. To hit the ball is known as a stroke. A golfer tries their best to complete the course in fewer than 74 strokes in order to win.

1. Fill in the missing values in the table above.

Marks: /4

2. Which of the players above won this game?

Answer: Marks: /1

3. How many strokes separated the best player and the worst player?

Answer: Marks: /2

4. If C. Jordan had hit 5 fewer strokes, would she have won?

Answer: Marks: /2

### Super Sleuth investigates

There are many different words used to describe the score that a golfer has achieved on one hole. If a golfer completes a par three hole in just two strokes, this is called a 'birdie'. We could write this as –1. Look up the following terms and work out how you would write them using directed numbers:

**1.** albatross, **2.** bogey, **3.** eagle, **4.** double bogey



Today's Marks: /9

# Day Four Try these.

CLUES

1. Fill in the missing values in this negative-numbers pyramid.

| | | | |
|---|---|---|---|
| | | | |
| | –21 | | |
| –9 | | –8 | |
| | –5 | | –1 |

Marks: /5

2. Write a word problem for which the answer will be –5. Write a number sentence to match your word problem.

Answer:

Marks: /2

3. 😀 is a number. I multiply it by 13 and add 15 to it. My answer is –89. What is the value of 😀?

Answer: Marks: /2

4. Write two questions for your group based on the image.

40 m
30 m
20 m
10 m
0 m
–10 m
–20 m
–30 m
–40 m

**Duties**

Reader
Calculator
Checker
Reporter

(a)

(b) Marks: /2

Today's Marks: /11

## Super Sleuth challenge

Organise a table quiz in your classroom. For every question answered correctly, a team will win 5 points. For every question answered incorrectly, a team will lose 3 points. At the end of each round, swap answer sheets and calculate the scores for your classmates.

Total Marks: /44 | I can explain what positive and negative numbers are. Yes ☐ No ☐

I can use positive and negative numbers. Yes ☐ No ☐

# 29 Data

**We are learning to:** Collect, organise and represent data using pie charts and trend graphs. ☐ Read and interpret trend graphs and pie charts. ☐ Gather data and represent it on a range of graphs and charts. ☐ Investigate averages. ☐

## Day One Try these.

CLUES

A survey was carried out in Newlands Senior Primary School to find out who the pupils' favourite authors were. The pie chart below shows the results.

1. If 40 children chose Roald Dahl as their favourite author, work out how many children took part in the survey altogether.

**Answer:** **Marks:** /2

2. Use your protractor to work out how many pupils chose each of the following authors as their favourite:

J.K. Rowling:

Eoin Colfer:

David Walliams:

Jacqueline Wilson:

Roald Dahl
Jacqueline Wilson
David Walliams
Eoin Colfer
J.K. Rowling

**Marks:** /4

3. What fraction of those surveyed chose a male author as their favourite? Write your answer in its lowest terms.

**Answer:** **Marks:** /2

### Puzzle power

If 15% of the pupils in Newlands Senior Primary School were absent on the day of the survey and 5% were at a football match, how many pupils are there altogether in the school?



**Today's Marks:** /8

## Day Two Try these.

1. Work in groups of 9, 12, 18 or 24 for this activity. Choose one of the questions below. Record the data that you collect within your group using a tally.

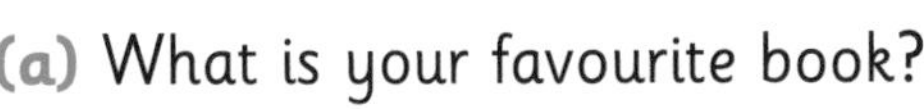

(a) What is your favourite book? (b) Who is your favourite band?
(c) What is your favourite colour? (d) What is your favourite gadget?

| | | |
|---|---|---|
| | | |
| | | |
| | | |
| | | |

Marks: /4

2. Represent the information that you collected above on the blank pie chart below.

**Top tip:**
Label your pie chart carefully. Use this key to identify the colours representing each sector of the chart.

Marks: /2

3. What is the average of 8.4, 6.1, 0.12 and 4.06?

Answer: Marks: /2

4. The average of 4 numbers is 24. If three of the numbers are 20, 11 and 27, what is the missing number? (Hint: Your first step is 24 x 4 = ____ Do you know why?)

Answer: Marks: /2

Today's Marks: /10

## Day Three

Try these.

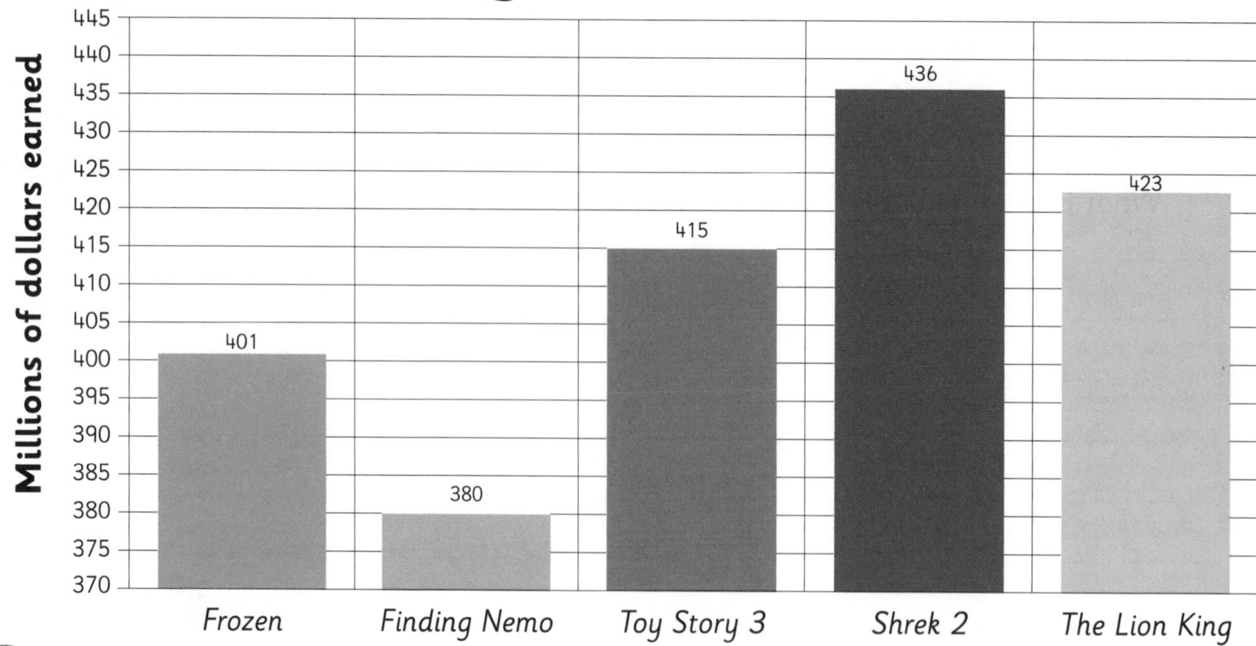


1. The graph above shows the earnings of the five highest-grossing children's films in US box office history as of 2016. Find the average earnings and draw a line indicating the average across the graph.

Answer: $ ______ Marks: /2

2. Name the films that earned less than the average earnings.

Answer: ______ Marks: /2

3. What is the difference between the highest-grossing film and **(a)** the average and **(b)** the lowest-grossing film?

Answers: (a) $ ______ (b) $ ______ Marks: /2

4. After this data was published, *Finding Dory* was released and earned more than *Shrek 2* in the US box office. If the average earnings of all six films was $423.5m, how much did *Finding Dory* earn?

Answer: $ ______ Marks: /2

Today's Marks: /8

## Day Four Try these.

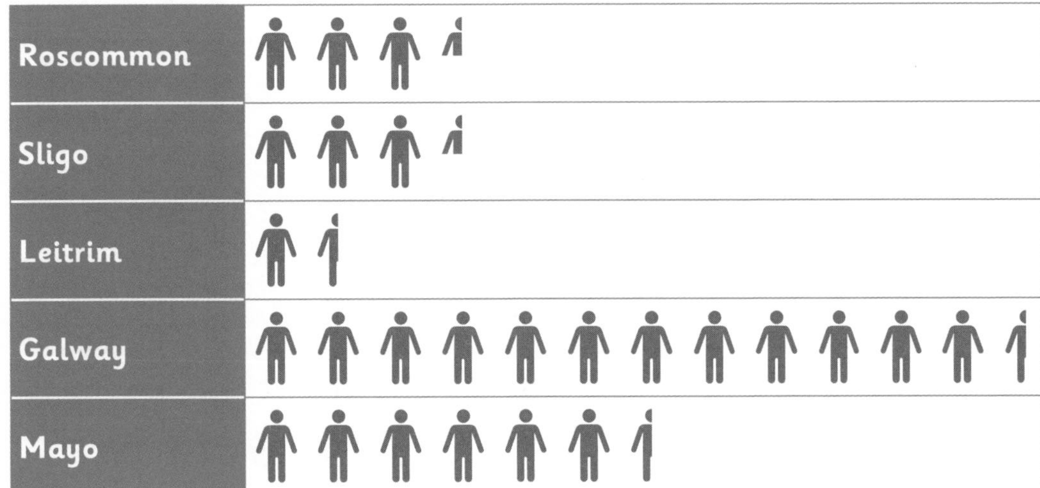


1. Look at the pictogram above. What do you think the data might represent? Discuss your thoughts with a partner.

Answer:

Marks: /2

2. The average is 32. What do you think the question might be? (There are many possible answers.)

Answer:

Marks: /2

3. The Green School Committee in 6th Class recorded the percentage of pupils in the school who travel to school in an environmentally-friendly manner each week. In your copy, show the following data on a trend graph:

| Date | April 14th | April 21st | April 28th | May 5th | May 12th | May 19th |
|---|---|---|---|---|---|---|
| Percentage | 58% | 62% | 64% | 67% | 48% | 70% |

Marks: /2

Today's Marks: /6

### Super Sleuth challenge

1. Discuss the trend graph that you drew for question 3 with a partner. What reasons might there be for the spikes and dips in the trend graph? Write five questions about the data. Swap with your partner and answer each other's questions.
2. Carry out a survey in your class to find out how your classmates travel to school over the course of a week. Represent the data that you collect on a trend graph.

Total Marks: /32 | In this unit, I most enjoyed

In this unit, I least enjoyed

# 30 Revision 5

## Day One

Here are the groups that have been drawn for the European Championships:

| Group A | Group B | Group C | Group D | Group E | Group F |
|---|---|---|---|---|---|
| Spain | Germany | France | Poland | Ukraine | Austria |
| Republic of Ireland | Belgium | England | Croatia | Czech Republic | Northern Ireland |
| Albania | Switzerland | Russia | Wales | Turkey | Sweden |
| Iceland | Hungary | Slovakia | Italy | Scotland | Finland |

**Try these.**

CLUES

1 (a) Assuming that all teams in the competition are of the same standard, work out the probability of a team with the word 'land' in its name winning the tournament. (b) Write it in percentage form rounded to two decimal places.

**Answers: (a)** ______ **(b)** ______ **Marks:** ___ /2

2 (a) Work out the likelihood of a team in group E winning the tournament. (b) Write it in fraction form. (c) Write it in percentage form rounded to one decimal place.

**Answers: (a)** ______ **(b)** ______ **(c)** ______ **Marks:** ___ /3

3 (a) What is the probability of a country whose name contains the letter 'a' winning the tournament? (b) Write it in fraction form. (c) Write it in percentage form rounded to the nearest whole number.

**Answers: (a)** ______ **(b)** ______ **(c)** ______ **Marks:** ___ /3

4 If 8 countries were added to the competition, what would the likelihood of one of the original countries winning the competition be? Write your answer in percentage form.

**Answer:** ______ **Marks:** ___ /2



Strand: Data Strand Units: Chance; Representing and Interpreting Data
Strand: Shape and Space Strand Unit: 3-D Shapes Strand: Algebra Strand Unit: Directed Numbers

**Today's Marks:** ___ /10

# Day Two Try these.

CLUES

1. Draw a net of each of the following 3-D shapes:

| (a) Tetrahedron | (b) Octahedron |
|---|---|
| (c) A prism of my choosing: | |

Using your drawings above as a guide, construct each net with an A4 sheet of paper and see if it makes the 3-D shape that you hoped it would. Label a vertex, an apex, an edge and a face on each model.

**Marks:** /6

2. If you were asked to colour the sides of a cuboid so that no two sides that are touching are the same colour, what is the fewest number of colours that you will need to use?

**Top tip:** Act it out with a cuboid.

**Answer:** **Marks:** /2

3. Make a 3-D model of a spaceship. Plan this activity by drawing nets of the shapes that you would like to use in the box provided. Include as many 3-D shapes as possible and label them. Use the names of these shapes when showing your model to your classmates.

**Marks:** /2

**Today's Marks:** /10

## Day Three Try these.

1. Give three examples of where directed numbers are used in real life.

| Answers: (a) | | (b) | | (c) | | Marks: | /3 |
|---|---|---|---|---|---|---|---|

2. Shauna went swimming with dolphins during a holiday in Florida. One of the dolphins could jump 2.95 m in the air and dive 5.75 m below sea level. What was the distance between the dolphin's jump and how far it dove below sea level? Draw this puzzle in a simple diagram. Label the sea level, the height to which the dolphin jumped and the depth to which it dove in your diagram.

Marks: /2

3. Once home from Florida, Shauna received her bank statement in the post. Use a calculator to find out if Shauna is in the red (in debt) or not.

Create your own puzzles for a partner based on Shauna's bank statement below.

| Date | Description | Debit | Credit | Balance |
|---|---|---|---|---|
| June 1st | Opening balance | | | €1,375 |
| June 2nd | Aer Lingus | €599 | | €776 |
| June 3rd | Sandals Resort Florida | €846.50 | | |
| June 4th | Lodgement | | €100 | |
| June 8th | MyTaxi | €21.80 | | |
| June 8th | Airport Cuisine | €15.20 | | |
| June 8th | Wages | | €1,010 | |
| June 9th | Currency exchange | €450.65 | | |
| June 10th | Dolphin Experience | €45.60 | | |
| June 11th | Helicopter School | €160.20 | | |
| June 13th | Disneyland | €346.90 | | |

Marks: /9



Today's Marks: /14

## Day Four Try these.

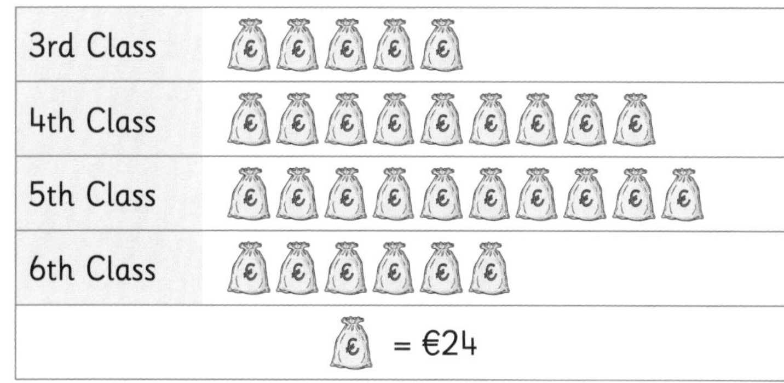

| | |
|---|---|
| 3rd Class | 💰💰💰💰💰 |
| 4th Class | 💰💰💰💰💰💰💰💰💰 |
| 5th Class | 💰💰💰💰💰💰💰💰💰💰 |
| 6th Class | 💰💰💰💰💰💰 |
| 💰 = €24 | |

Holywell Senior Primary School raised money for charity. Use the pictogram above to answer the questions below.

1. How much money did each class raise for charity?

| 3rd Class | 4th Class | 5th Class | 6th Class |
|---|---|---|---|
| € | € | € | € |

Marks: /4

2. What fraction of the entire amount collected did each class raise?

Answers: 3rd Class 4th Class 5th Class 6th Class Marks: /4

3. What was the average amount of money raised per class?

Answer: € Marks: /2

4. Use a compass and a protractor to draw a pie chart illustrating the information in the pictogram above.

Marks: /4

Today's Marks: /14

Total Marks: /48